Framework 7

MATHS C

HOMEWORK BOOK

David Capewell	Westfield School, Sheffield
Marguerite Comyns	Queen Mary's High School, Walsall
Gillian Flinton	All Saints Catholic High School, Sheffield
Geoff Fowler	Maths Strategy Manager, Birmingham
Kam Grewal-Joy	Mathematics Consultant
Derek Huby	Mathematics Consultant
Peter Johnson	Wellfield High School, Leyland, Lancashire
Penny Jones	Mathematics Consultant, Birmingham
Jayne Kranat	Langley Park School for Girls, Bromley
Ian Molyneux	St. Bedes RC High School, Ormskirk
Peter Mullarkey	School Improvement Officer, Manchester
Nina Patel	Ifield Community College, West Sussex

OXFORD
UNIVERSITY PRESS

OXFORD

UNIVERSITY PRESS

Great Clarendon Street, Oxford OX2 6DP

Oxford University Press is a department of the University of Oxford.
It furthers the University's objective of excellence in research,
scholarship, and education by publishing worldwide in

Oxford New York

Auckland Bangkok Buenos Aires Cape Town Chennai
Dar es Salaam Delhi Hong Kong Istanbul Karachi Kolkata
Kuala Lumpur Madrid Melbourne Mexico City Mumbai
Nairobi São Paulo Shanghai Taipei Tokyo Toronto

Oxford is a registered trade mark of Oxford University Press
in the UK and in certain other countries

British Library Cataloguing in Publication Data

Data available

ISBN 0 19 914885 6

10 9 8 7 6 5 4 3

The photograph on the cover is reproduced courtesy of
Pictor International (UK)

The publishers would like to thank QCA for their kind permission to use
Key Stage 3 SAT questions.

Typeset by Tech-Set Ltd, Gateshead, Tyne and Wear

Printed in Great Britain by Bell and Bain, Glasgow

About this book

Framework Maths Year 7C has been written specifically for Year 7 of the Framework for Teaching Mathematics. It is aimed at students who are following the Year 7 teaching programme from the Framework and have gained a Level 4 at the end of KS2.

The authors are experienced teachers and maths consultants, who have been incorporating the Framework approaches into their teaching for many years and so are well qualified to help you successfully meet the Framework objectives.

The books are made up of units based on the medium-term plans that complement the Framework document, thus maintaining the required pitch, pace and progression.

This Homework Book is written to support the Core objectives in Year 7, and is designed to support the use of the Framework Maths Year 7C Student's Book.

The material is ideal for homework, further work in class and extra practice. It comprises:
◆ A homework for every lesson, with a focus on problem-solving activities.
◆ Worked examples as appropriate, so the book is self-contained.
◆ Past paper SAT questions at the end of each unit, at Level 4 and Level 5 so that you can check students' progress against National Standards.

Problem solving is integrated throughout the material as suggested in the Framework.

Contents

1   For each sequence copy and complete the statements.

   a   5, 10, 15, 20, 25, …

   The first term is ____5____

   The rule is ____n+5____

   b   1, 5, 9, 13, 17, …

   The first term is ___1___

   The rule is ____n+4____

   c   20, 17, 14, 11, …

   The first term is ___20___

   The rule is ___n-3___

   The fifth term is ___8___

   d   8, 10, 12, 14, 16, 18

   The first term is ___8___

   Fill in the missing numbers.

   The rule is ____n+2____

2   Fill in the missing numbers *and* describe the following sequences:

   a   2, 5, _7_, 11, 14, _19_, _22_ ✗

   b   30, 25, _20_, _15_, 10, _5_

   c   1, 4, 9, 16, ____

   d   2, 4, ____, 16, 32, ____

   e   100, 50, ____, 12.5

   f   18, ____, ____, 27, 30

1   Find the missing terms in these sequences.

    a   4, 6, ____, 10, ____, 14, ____   **b**   8, 11, ____, ____, ____, 23

    c   ____, ____, 5, ____, ____, 11   **d**   5, ____, ____, 14, 17, ____, ____

    e   1, 2, 4, 7, 11, ____, ____   **f**   1, 2, 4, 8, ____, ____

    g   1, 4, 9, 16, 25, ____, ____   **h**   1, 3, 6, 10, 15, ____, ____

2   Each of the numbers in the box belongs to one of the sequences A, B, C or D.

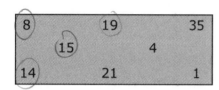

    Sort each number into one of the four sequences.

    A   The first term is 5, each term is 3 larger.   8,14

    B   The first term is 7, each term is 4 larger.   15,19

    C   The first term is 19, each term is 5 less.

    D   The first term is 9, each term is 4 larger.

    Which numbers appear in more than one sequence?

3   Find three different sequences that start 2, 4, …
    Now describe each of your sequences in words.

              numbers.

4   The first five terms from two sequences have been jumbled up together to make the list
    below. Find these two sequences and then define each in words.
                           rule.

    23   13   11   17   17   25   5   29   29   21

        5 , 11 , 17 , 23 , 29

Mix and match

Here are three tables (1, 2 and 3) and three patterns (A, B and C).

1

Pattern number	1	2	3	4	5	6	7	8
Number of matches/counters	8	14						

2

Pattern number	1	2	3	4	5	6	7	8
Number of matches/counters	5		11					

3

Pattern number	1	2	3	4	5	6	7	8
Number of matches/counters	4	7	10	13	16	19	22	25

Start at 4 and add 3 eachtime.

(a) Pattern A goes with table 3.

$15^{th} = 15 \times 3 + 1$

A

4   7   10

B

   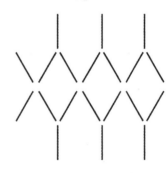

C

a Match each set of patterns with the correct table and complete the table.

b Explain in words how each pattern is increasing.

c Predict how many matches/counters will be required for the 9th pattern.

d Explain in words how you would find the number of matches/counters for the 15th pattern. (Use as few words as possible.)

A   In this function machine, the input is 7 and the output is 3:

$$7 \longrightarrow \boxed{+ 2} \longrightarrow \boxed{÷ 3} \longrightarrow 3$$

$$7 + 2 = 9 \qquad 9 ÷ 3 = 3$$

Find the output for these function machines:

1 $$3 \longrightarrow \boxed{× 4} \longrightarrow \boxed{+ 2} \longrightarrow ?$$

2 $$7 \longrightarrow \boxed{+ 2} \longrightarrow \boxed{× 5} \longrightarrow ?$$

3 $$36 \longrightarrow \boxed{÷ 3} \longrightarrow \boxed{+ 7} \longrightarrow ?$$

4 $$15 \longrightarrow \boxed{× 5} \longrightarrow \boxed{- 27} \longrightarrow ?$$

5 $$13 \longrightarrow \boxed{× 4} \longrightarrow \boxed{- 7} \longrightarrow ?$$

6 $$11 \longrightarrow \boxed{× 8} \longrightarrow \boxed{+ 15} \longrightarrow ?$$

B   Find the input for these function machines:

7 $$? \longrightarrow \boxed{× 2} \longrightarrow \boxed{- 1} \longrightarrow 5$$

8 $$? \longrightarrow \boxed{× 4} \longrightarrow \boxed{- 3} \longrightarrow 9$$

9 $$? \longrightarrow \boxed{× 5} \longrightarrow \boxed{- 7} \longrightarrow 28$$

10 $$? \longrightarrow \boxed{× 8} \longrightarrow \boxed{- 4} \longrightarrow 36$$

11 $$? \longrightarrow \boxed{× 3} \longrightarrow \boxed{+ 2} \longrightarrow 29$$

12 $$? \longrightarrow \boxed{× 4} \longrightarrow \boxed{- 5} \longrightarrow 39$$

1   Use only two of the shaded operations to make each of the function machines **a** to **e** total 20.

a   2 ⟶ ▭ ▭ ⟶ 20

b   3 ⟶ ▭ ▭ ⟶ 20

c   8 ⟶ ▭ ▭ ⟶ 20

d   12 ⟶ ▭ ▭ ⟶ 20

e   17 ⟶ ▭ ▭ ⟶ 20

Challenge

2   The aim is to make all the outputs from 1 to 10 with an input of 4 in this two-stage function machine.

4 ⟶ ▭ ▭ ⟶   1 2 3 4 5

                          6 7 8 9 10

You may use any of the four operations ($+$, $-$, $\div$, $\times$) with any of the numbers 1, 2, 3, 4.

For example,

4 ⟶ $\times 2$ ⟶ $- 1$ ⟶ 7

Write the output for these function machines as algebraic expressions. For example,

$$n \longrightarrow \boxed{\times 2} \longrightarrow \boxed{+ 3} \longrightarrow ?$$

The output is $n \times 2 + 3$, or $2n + 3$.

1 $n \longrightarrow \boxed{\times 5} \longrightarrow ?$

2 $n \longrightarrow \boxed{+ 4} \longrightarrow ?$

3 $n \longrightarrow \boxed{- 5} \longrightarrow ?$

4 $n \longrightarrow \boxed{\div 2} \longrightarrow ?$

5 $n \longrightarrow \boxed{\times 3} \longrightarrow \boxed{+ 1} \longrightarrow ?$

6 $n \longrightarrow \boxed{\div 4} \longrightarrow \boxed{- 2} \longrightarrow ?$

7 $n \longrightarrow \boxed{\div 3} \longrightarrow \boxed{+ 6} \longrightarrow ?$

8 $n \longrightarrow \boxed{\text{square}} \longrightarrow \boxed{+ 6} \longrightarrow ?$

9 $n \longrightarrow \boxed{\times \frac{1}{2}} \longrightarrow \boxed{+ 2} \longrightarrow ?$

10 $n \longrightarrow \boxed{\times {}^{-}2} \longrightarrow \boxed{- 5} \longrightarrow ?$

Challenge

11 Draw a function machine for these expressions:

    a $n + 7$

    b $2n$

    c $\dfrac{n}{2}$

    d $4n + 1$

Level 4

Owen has some tiles like these:

He uses the tiles to make a series of patterns.

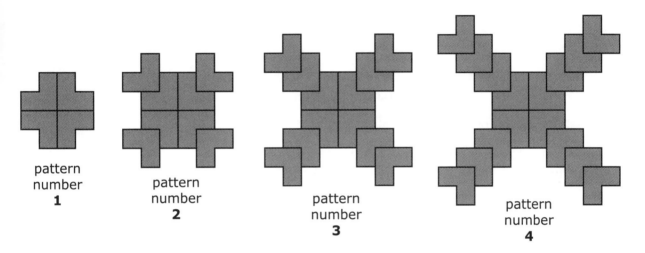

pattern
number
1

pattern
number
2

pattern
number
3

pattern
number
4

a Each new pattern has **more tiles** than the one before.
The number of tiles goes up by the same amount each time.

How many **more** tiles does Owen add each time he
makes a new pattern?   *1 mark*

b **How many tiles** will Owen need altogether to make
pattern number 6?   *1 mark*

c **How many tiles** will Owen need altogether to make
pattern number 9?   *1 mark*

d Owen uses **40 tiles** to make a pattern.
What is the **number** of the **pattern** he makes?   *1 mark*

Level 5

These patterns are made with matchsticks.

1 triangle   2 triangles   3 triangles
3 matchsticks   5 matchsticks   7 matchsticks

Every pattern is made with an odd number of matchsticks.
The rule for finding the number of **matchsticks** in a pattern is:

2 times the number of triangles, **add 1**.

a Jason wants to make the pattern with **9** triangles.
     Use the rule to find how many matchsticks he will need. *1 mark*

b **M** = number of **matchsticks**
     T = number of **triangles**

     Use symbols to write down the rule connecting **M** and **T**. *1 mark*

c The rule for finding the number of **triangles** in a pattern is:

     The number matchsticks **take away 1**, then **divide by 2**.

     Bethan uses **11** matchsticks to make a pattern.

     Use the rule to find how many triangles she has in her
     pattern.   *1 mark*

d Misa uses **35** matchsticks to make a pattern.

     Use the rule to find how many triangles she has in her
     pattern.   *1 mark*

Complete question 1 OR question 2:

1 Different civilisations in history have used different number systems.

The Romans used a system of letters for numbers of different values.

I = 1	V = 5
X = 10	L = 50
C = 100	D = 500
M = 1000	

They also used place value in a different way.

A letter of lower value before a bigger one meant subtraction.
For example: IV = V–I = 5–1 = 4

A letter of lower value after a bigger one meant addition.
For example: VI = V+I = 5+1 = 6

a Put these Roman numbers in order, smallest first:
I IX II V VI III VIII X IV VII

b Write the year of your birth in Roman numbers.
For example, 1990 would be MDCCCCXC.

c Put these numbers on a number line (1 to 100):
V L LV LXXI XX C XL

2 **a** Find out about number systems from other civilisations.
You should research at least two systems.
For example, you might research:
- Ancient Egyptian numbers
- Roman numbers
- Mayan numbers
- Gujurati numbers.

You may find some information in an encyclopaedia in the library
or you could search the internet.

b Write a short report on your findings.
The report may include:
- A description of the number systems
- When they were used and by whom
- What made them easy to use
- What made them difficult to use
- A comparison of the systems.

The graph shows the changes in height of two nearby islands relative to sea level.

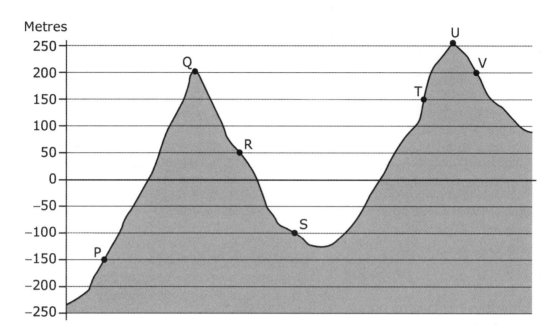

1   Work out these changes in height.

  a   From R to S
  b   From T to V
  c   From S to T
  d   From P to R
  e   From U to V
  f   From T to U
  g   From P to R
  h   From Q to S
  i   From P to V

2   What is the maximum depth of the sea between the two islands?

3   Captain Bluebeard sits at point Q and looks over to the top of the next island at point U.

  a   Is it higher or lower?
  b   What is the difference in height?

Look at the number grid shown.

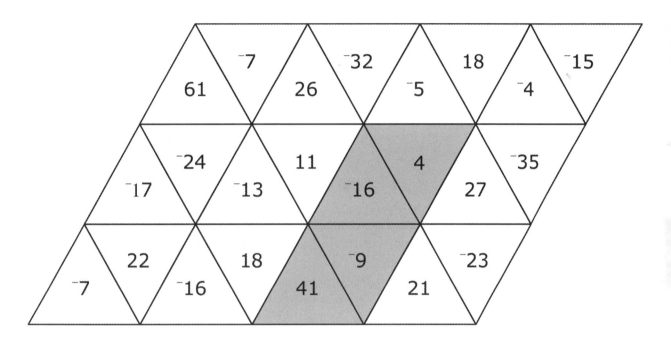

The shaded shape is a four-number parallelogram.

The numbers in the parallelogram add up to 41 + ⁻9 + ⁻16 + 4 = 20

1   Which four-number parallelogram has the highest total?

2   Which four-number parallelogram has the lowest total?

For you to do . . .

Design a poster to explain how to:

◆ Add decimals mentally such as 15.2 + 6.3

◆ Subtract decimals mentally such as 12.8 − 4.9

Your poster should describe the different methods you can use.

Your methods should include:

◆ Partitioning

◆ Compensation

Here is a reminder:

Partitioning	253 + 325
Write the larger number first for addition	325 + 253
Break the smaller number into place value parts	325 + 200 + 50 + 3
Add/subtract the 100s Add/subtract the tens Add/subtract the units	525 + 50 + 3 575 + 3 578
So:	253 + 325 = 578

Compensation	276 + 398
Round the number and write the compensation	276 + 400 − 2
Use the rounding	676 − 2
Then compensate	674
So:	276 + 398 = 674

This square has a number written at each of its corners:

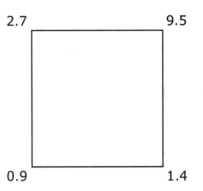

1   Calculate the difference between each pair of corner numbers and write it in the middle of the appropriate side.

2   Join these middle numbers to make a new square inside the first square.

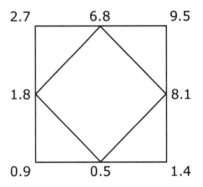

3   Now repeat the process for the new square.

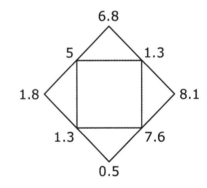

4   Repeat the process until you reach zero.

   ◆   **Investigate** how many steps it takes for different starting numbers.

   ◆   Can you **predict** how many steps it will take just by looking at the starting numbers?

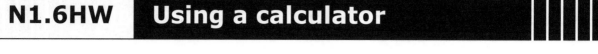

1 Estimate the number that the arrow is pointing to:

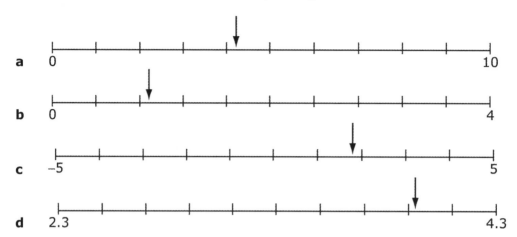

2 Ravi records how long it takes him to get to work one particular week.
These are his times:

35 minutes, an hour and a quarter, three quarters of an hour,
50 minutes, an hour and 5 minutes.

a Use a mental or written method to find the total length of time Ravi took in getting to work that week.

b Key 'an hour and a quarter' into your calculator.
What does the display read?

3 Fiona records her weekly shopping bill over 6 weeks.

These are the amounts: £73.12, £58.24, £81.96, £79.03, £49.35, £56.22

a Work out the total amount she spent on shopping over these six weeks.

b She originally budgeted for £400 in total. Was this amount sufficient?
Explain your answer.

4 Calculate the following using a mental or written method, or where appropriate using your calculator.

Estimate first.

a $7.621 + 3.49$

b $15.7 - (2.81 + 3.97 + 8.2 + 6.19)$

c $23.84 - {}^{-}15.21$

d $\dfrac{9.2 - 5.8}{9.2 + 5.8}$

e $29.91 - (10.1 - 19.04)$

Look at these three signs:

<		=		>
is **less** than		is **equal** to		is **greater** than

Examples:

$$5 < 6 \qquad 4 - 3 = 2 - 1 \qquad 6 - 2 > 9 - 6$$

5 is **less** than 6   4 – 3 is **equal** to 2 – 1   6 – 2 is **greater** than 9 – 6

Put the correct **sign**, < or = or >, into each number sentence.

a   8 + 2 _____ 7 + 6   **b**   6 – 3 _____ 1 + 2

c   0 _____ ‾3   **d**   ‾7 _____ ‾2

e   3 – 2 _____ ‾5   **f**   5 – 5 _____ 4 – 6   *6 marks*

Look at these number cards:

| +3 | 0 | −5 | +9 | +2 | −8 | +7 | −2 |

a   Choose a card to give the answer 4.

$$\boxed{+2} + \boxed{-5} + \boxed{} = 4$$

1 mark

b   Choose a card to give the **lowest** possible answer.
      Copy and fill in the cards below and work out the answer.

$$\boxed{-2} - \boxed{} = \underline{\hspace{2cm}}$$

2 marks

Remember:

◆ Area of a rectangle = length × breadth
  A = $l \times b$

◆ Perimeter is the distance around a shape (it is a **length**)

◆ Units for area are mm², cm², ft² etc.

◆ The range = highest value – lowest value

Find the area and perimeter of these shapes:

1 **a**

12 m
15 m

b

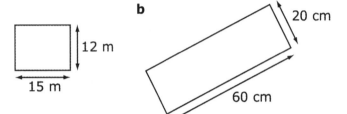

20 cm
60 cm

c

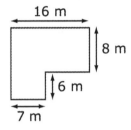

16 m
8 m
6 m
7 m

2 The area of this stamp is 10 cm².
The length is 5 cm.

What is the width?

3 Calculate the area and perimeter of this rectangle.
Be careful with the units.

Give your area:

a in cm²   **b** in mm²

What do you notice?

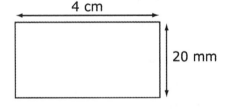

4 cm
20 mm

4 Estimate the area of this shape. Use the following method:

◆ Trace the shape onto paper.

◆ Draw a rectangle outside the shape.

◆ Draw a rectangle inside the shape.

◆ Find the area of each rectangle.

◆ Use your answers to estimate the area.

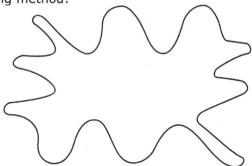

Remember:

◆ Area of a right-angled triangle
  $= \frac{1}{2} \times$ base $\times$ height

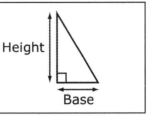

1 A triangle has an area 50 cm². Its base is 5 cm. What is its height?

2 A right-angled isosceles triangle has area 8 mm².

What are the lengths of the two equal sides?

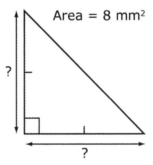

Area = 8 mm²

3 Find the area of these compound shapes.

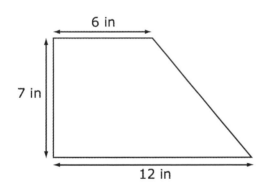

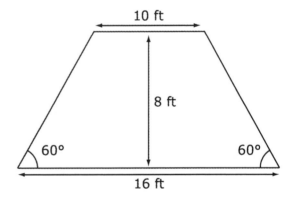

4 Find the area and perimeter of a path 1 m wide bordering the outside of a 6 m² lawn.

5 Carpet tiles 1 metre square are to be used to cover a rectangular lounge 6 metres by 5 metres. How many tiles will be needed?

6 20 cm tiles are to be used in a bathroom to cover a wall 3 m by 2 m.
How many tiles are needed?

Choose four objects you can see so that:

◆   One is small enough to carry it in your hand.

◆   One is too large to carry.

◆   One is between the other two.

The other one is of your own choice.

Complete the table for each of your objects.

object	units	equipment	Estimated length	Estimated width	Estimated area	Actual length	Actual width	Actual area

Write the units you would use to measure your object here.

Write the equipment you'd need to measure each object accurately.

Estimate the length and the width. Use your answers to estimate the area of the front of each object.

Measure the actual length and width. Use your measurements to find the actual area of the front of each object.

Remember:

- You can describe a 3-D shape by its faces, edges and vertices.
- A net is a flat shape that folds up into a 3-D shape. The area of the net of a 3-D shape is called the surface area.

For each shape:

- Write down the number of faces, edges and vertices it has
- Draw an accurate net
- Find its surface area

a cube

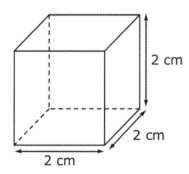

b triangular prism

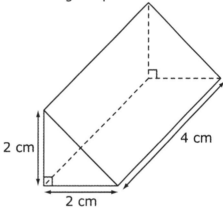

c cuboid

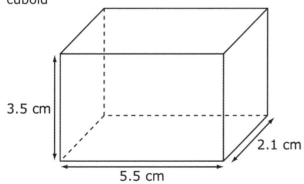

Level 4

In this question, each square represents 1cm².

The shaded rectangle has an **area** of **4 cm²** and a **perimeter** of **10 cm**.

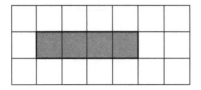

a Look at the cross-shape.

Find the **area** in **cm²** and the **perimeter** in **cm** of the cross-shape.

2 marks

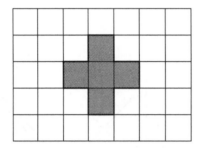

b On a square grid draw a shape with an **area** of **6 cm²**.

1 mark

c What is the **perimeter** of your shape?

1 mark

d Look at the octagon.

What is the area of the octagon?

1 mark

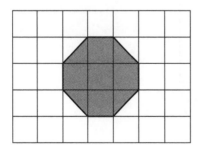

e Explain how you know that the perimeter of the octagon **is more than 8 cm**.

1 mark

a Which of the rectangles below have an area of 12 cm²?

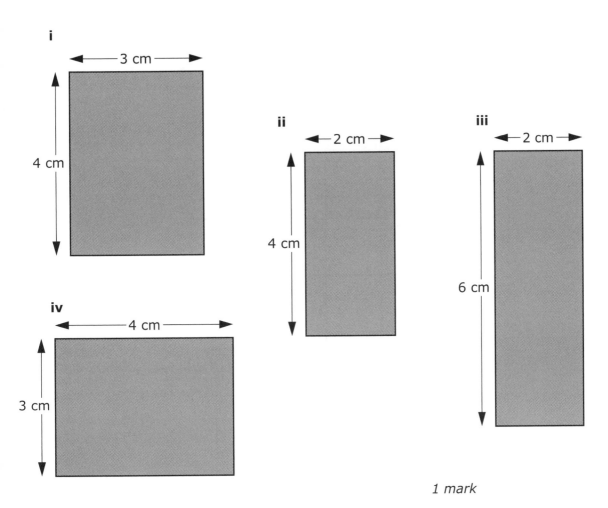

1 mark

b A **square** has an area of **100 cm²**.

What is its **perimeter**? *Show your working.*   *2 marks*

Find as many different ways as you can of dividing this 4 × 4 square into quarters using only straight lines.

You should be able to find at least 3.

Here is an example:

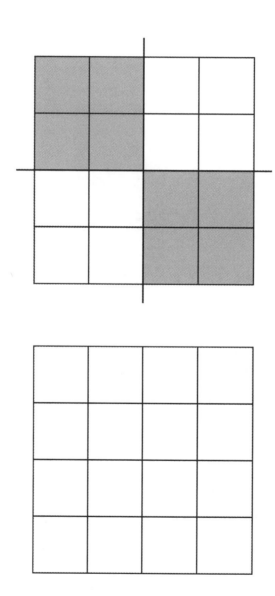

Equivalent fractions

For you to do...

Design a poster to show that:

◆ $\frac{8}{12}$ is equivalent to $\frac{6}{9}$ or $\frac{4}{6}$ or $\frac{2}{3}$.

For example:

$$\frac{4}{12} = \frac{3}{9} = \frac{1}{3}$$

Here is a cake divided into pieces:

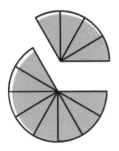 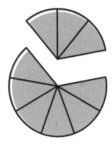 

The pieces are all the same size in total.

Therefore the fractions are equivalent.

You could use a different fraction, with a cake if you want.

Or you could use shaded shapes, or a jug of water divided into different amounts.

Ferry crossings

Tom works for a ferry company.

His job is to position the vehicles on the boat.

His ferry can load 3 rows of vehicles.

Each row is a maximum of 10 m long.

| Lane 1 |
| Lane 2 |
| Lane 3 |

$\longleftarrow$ 10 m $\longrightarrow$

There are 10 vehicles waiting to use the ferry, and they have the following lengths in metres:

Car and trailer	$\frac{154}{40}$	$3\frac{3}{5}$	$\frac{32}{10}$	$3\frac{4}{8}$	$\frac{15}{4}$
Van	$\frac{29}{4}$	$6\frac{3}{20}$	$\frac{25}{4}$		
Motorbike	$\frac{27}{20}$	$\frac{7}{5}$			

1   How can Tom fill Lane 1?
(Hint: Why not convert everything to mixed numbers first?
Then add the whole numbers, and then add the fractions.)

2   How can Tom fill Lane 2?

3   Is there now enough space left in Lane 3 for the rest of the vehicles? Explain your answer.

Investigation

In a room there are three tables, each with 10 chairs around them.

On Table 1 there is one chocolate bar.

On Table 2 there are two chocolate bars.

On Table 3 there are three chocolate bars.

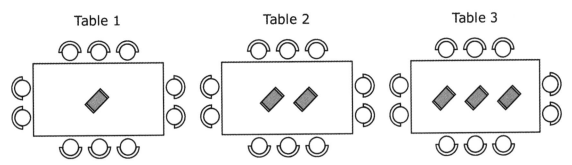

There are 10 people waiting to enter the room one at a time.

Each person must choose to sit at one of the tables.

After all 10 people have entered, the chocolate on each table is shared between the people sat around it.

1 Investigate where each person should sit to get the most chocolate as they enter the room.

For example:

Person 1 sits at Table 3 because it has the most chocolate.

If Person 2 sat at :

◆ Table 1 – 1 bar

◆ Table 2 – 2 bars

◆ Table 3 – $\frac{3}{2}$ bars.

So they sit at Table 2.....

2 Investigate what happens if six more people enter the room one at a time.

Puzzle: Uncle Peter's Rabbit

When their father died, the three sons of Albert Hodwinckle were left 17 rabbits.

The rabbits had to be shared according to their father's will:

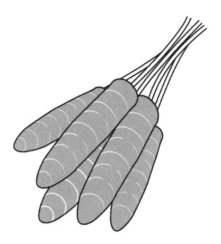

'My eldest son shall receive $\frac{1}{2}$ of my rabbits.'

'My second son shall receive $\frac{1}{3}$ of my rabbits.'

'My youngest son shall receive $\frac{1}{9}$ of my rabbits.'

The sons found it difficult to share out the rabbits according to their father's instructions, as none of the rabbits was to be harmed.

Eventually the sons went to visit their Uncle Peter, who said he would lend them his pet rabbit Veggie, but that Veggie had to be returned at the end of the day.

1 How did the sons fulfil their father's wishes and divide up the rabbits in the correct fractions?

2 Which one of the sons should receive Veggie as part of their share, and return Veggie to Uncle Peter?

Explain your reasoning.

Loop cards

Design a set of loop cards to practise learning the equivalence of fractions, decimals and percentages. Here is an example of a loop card.

Answer	Question
$\frac{1}{5}$	45%

A complete loop of four would look like this:

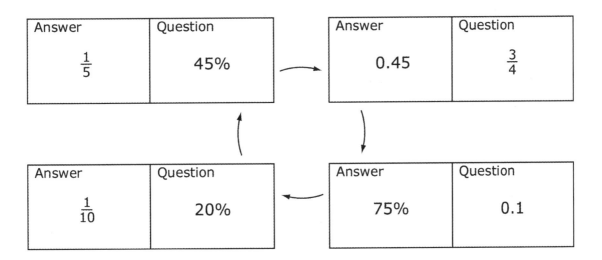

You should try to create a loop of 10.

Level 4

Some pupils are climbing up the ropes of the gym.

These are their positions after climbing for a few seconds.

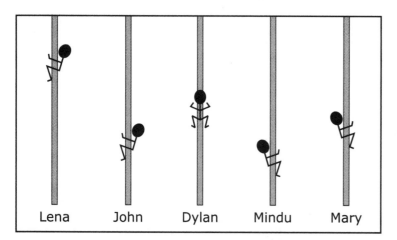

Lena   John   Dylan   Mindu   Mary

a   Dylan is about $\frac{1}{2}$ of the way **up** the rope.

Copy these sentences and fill each gap with a fraction.

i   Lena is about ___$\frac{4}{5}$___ of the way up the rope.   *1 mark*

ii   John is about ___$\frac{1}{3}$___ of the way up the rope.   *1 mark*

b   Dylan is about 50% of the way **up** the rope.

Copy these sentences and fill each gap with a percentage.

i   Mindu is about __20·__ % of the way up the rope.   *1 mark*

ii   Mary is about __40·__ % of the way up the rope.   *1 mark*

c   Anna is climbing a longer rope.

She has climbed $\frac{2}{5}$ of the way up the rope.

Draw Anna's rope and put a **X** on the rope to show her position.

1 mark

Anna

$\frac{1}{2}$ of the diagram below is shaded.

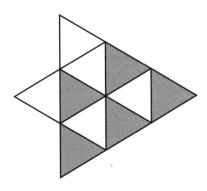

a Look at this diagram:

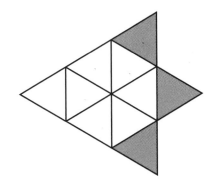

$\frac{3}{10}$ 30%

i	What **fraction** is shaded?	*1 mark*
ii	What **percentage** is shaded?	*1 mark*
b **i**	Copy the diagram below and shade $\frac{2}{5}$ of it.	*1 mark*

ii What **percentage** of the diagram have you shaded? *1 mark* 40%

> **Remember:**
> ◆ The mode is the value in the data that occurs most often.
> ◆ The median is the value in the middle of the data.
>   The data must be arranged in order first.
> ◆ The range = highest value – lowest value

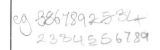

1   Work out the median, mode and range of these sets of data.

For each set decide what the information could represent and who might use it.

a   3°C, 2°C, 4°C, 3°C, 1°C, –1°C, 3°C, –2°C, 2°C

b   11 mm, 13 mm, 10 mm, 9 mm, 11 mm, 12 mm, 15 mm, 15 mm, 10 mm, 11 mm, 10 mm, 8 mm, 13 mm, 15 mm, 10 mm, 11 mm

c   3.1 g, 2.4 g, 2.5 g, 3.4 g, 2.7 g, 3.2 g, 2.5 g, 3.1 g, 2.6 g, 3.5 g, 2.5 g, 3.1 g, 3.2 g, 2.5 g, 3.0 g, 2.5 g, 3.1 g, 2.3 g, 3.3 g, 2.5 g, 3.1 g

2   Work out the median and mode of these sets of data.

Decide which average is most typical of each set of data giving a reason for your answer.

a   Shoe sizes of a pop group: 5, 7, 8, 6, 4, 7, 5

b   Heights of children at a playgroup: 98 cm, 105 cm, 120 cm, 95 cm, 107 cm, 125cm, 119 cm, 125 cm, 100 cm

c   Cost of a packet of crisps: 25p, 30p, 32p, 24p, 26p, 25p, 23p, 31p, 27p, 28p, 25p, 26p

d   Length of TV programmes one evening: 30 mins, 50 mins, 30 mins, 1 hour, 40 mins, 1 hour, 20 mins, 1 hour 35 mins, 5 mins, 2 hours

3   The tally chart shows the price of different chocolate bars in a sweet shop, in March and April. Work out the median and the mode of the price for each month.

Price of a chocolate bar	March	April
28p	||	|||
30p	|||	||||
32p	||	
35p	|||	||
36p				

Remember:

◆ The mean of a set of data is the sum of all the values divided by the number of values.

1 Find the mean for each of these sets of data:

    a Shoe sizes: 5, 4, 10, 3, 3, 4, 7, 4, 6, 5

    b Dress sizes: 10, 12, 10, 18, 12, 14, 12

    c Hours of sunshine one week: 4, 5, 3, 4, 5, 0, 1

    d Daily temperatures one week: 17, 25, 22, 18, 22, 16, 19

2 The England selectors have to choose a new batsman for the next test match.

The aim of a good batsman is to score as high a total as possible over two innings.

The table gives their current performance.

Player	Match 1		Match 2		Match 3	
	1st innings	2nd innings	1st innings	2nd innings	1st innings	2nd innings
A	52	47	63	0	99	45
B	65	51	20	39	100	–
C	48	70	5	53	86	62
D	53	8	68	–	75	–

'–' means the batsman did not bat and so the first innings is counted as their average for that match.

Which one would you advise them to choose? Give a reason for your answer.

3 Use your knowledge of the mean to answer these questions.

    a Imran scored an average of 4 goals from 5 matches.
       How many goals did he score altogether?

    b 10 lengths of fabric are cut from a roll of fabric.
       The mean length of fabric is 4 m.
       How many metres are cut altogether?

    c The mean of 4 playing cards showing 1, 8, 5 and 2 is 4.
       Another card is drawn from the pack and the mean remains 4.
       What is the value of the new card?

This line graph shows the percentage of people committing an offence in 1997–98, for both males and females in England and Wales.

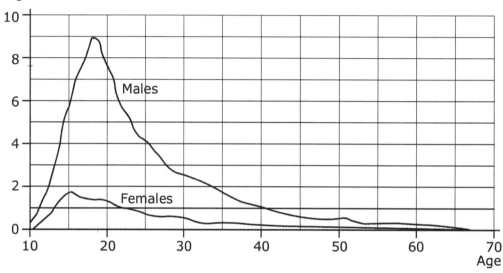

Source: Home Office

1 **a** At what age is the highest percentage of male offenders? 18

　　b At what age is the highest percentage of female offenders? 16

2 **a** What percentage of 20 year old males are offenders? 7%

　　b How is your answer to part **a** different for female offenders?

　　c How many times higher is the offence rate for 20 year old males than for 20 year old females?

3 Why do you think the graph 'tails off' at older age groups?

4 Write a short report on what this graph shows.
　　Use terms like 'percentage' and 'mode'.

Bags of beads

Class 7C are playing a game of chance with a bag of beads.

There are two teams: the boys and the girls.

Their teacher has three bags of black and white beads.

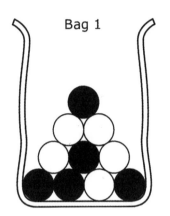 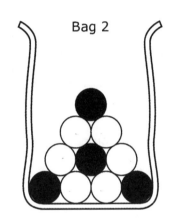 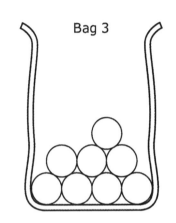

Bag 1   Bag 2   Bag 3

◆ She pulls a bead out of one of her bags.

   ◆ If it is white the boys get a point.

   ◆ If it is black the girls get a point.

◆ She then puts the bead back and pulls out another one.

◆ The first team to get 20 points wins the game.

1 Which team is most likely to win the game if the teacher uses:

  a bag 1   **b** bag 2   **c** bag 3?

Give your reasons. *because all the beads inside are what which means no black for the boys*

2 Mark the probabilities of these events on a number line from 0 to 1. Use fractions.

  A: The girls win using bag 1 $\frac{1}{2}$ D: The boys win using bag 1 $\frac{1}{2}$

  B: The girls win using bag 2 ✓   E: The boys win using bag 2

  C: The girls win using bag 3 ✓   F: The boys win using bag 3

0   1

A box of chocolates contains 12 soft centres and 8 hard centres.

The probability of picking a hard centre is $\frac{8}{20}$ or 0.4.

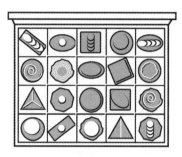

You eat a number of chocolates.

1 What combination of chocolates could you eat so that the probability of picking a hard centre becomes $\frac{1}{2}$?

List all the possibilities.

2 a What is the smallest number of chocolates you would need to eat so that the probability of picking a soft centre is twice that of picking a hard centre?

b What is the greatest number you could eat to make the probability of picking a soft centre twice that of picking a hard centre?

3 You eat six chocolates.
List all the possible combinations of chocolates left in the box.

For each combination:

◆ write down the probability of getting a soft centre

◆ write down the probability of getting a hard centre.

What do you notice about the two probabilities in each case?
Explain what you notice.

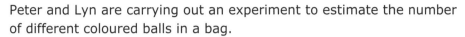

Peter and Lyn are carrying out an experiment to estimate the number of different coloured balls in a bag.

◆ They take it in turns to draw a ball from the bag.

◆ They note its colour and record it in a table.

◆ They then replace the ball in the bag.

◆ They repeat this 10 times.

◆ The bag contains 20 balls in total.

Here are their results:

Colour	Tally	Frequency
Blue	|||	3
Green	||	2
Red	||||	4
Yellow	|	1

1 Use the results to estimate the probability of drawing each colour ball from the bag.

2 a How many would you expect to be yellow? 2

b How many would you expect to be red? 8

c How many would you expect to be green? 4

d How many would you expect to be blue? 6

Explain your choice in each case.

3 How many of each colour would you expect there to be if the bag contains 25 balls?

4 Explain how you could find a better estimate for the probability of picking each ball.

A machine in a youth club sells snacks.

Len writes down the amounts of money that different people spend one evening during each hour that the club is open:

Crisps:	20p
Chocolate bars:	35p
Drinks:	40p
Rolls:	75p
Sandwiches:	£1.00

Amounts of money spent each hour		
5 pm to 6 pm	**6 pm to 7 pm**	**7 pm to 8 pm**
40p	75p	£1.75
60p	55p	£1.40
55p	60p	£1.60
20p	40p	75p
40p	£1.15	£1.40
60p	40p	£1.10
55p	75p	60p
40p	40p	£1.50

a Len says: '**40p** is the **mode** of the amounts of money spent.'
Explain why Len is **right**. *1 mark*

b Len groups the amounts and starts to make a tally chart.
Copy Len's chart and fill it in for 7 pm to 8 pm.
Then fill in the column for the **total** number of people who spent each amount. *2 marks*

Amount of money spent	Time			Total number of people
	5 pm to 6 pm	**6 pm to 7 pm**	**7 pm to 8 pm**	
Under 50p	IIII	III		7
50p to 99p	IIII	IIII		
£1.00 to £1.49		I		
Over £1.49				

c Len says: 'Now **50p to 99p** is the **mode**.'
Is Len right? Explain your answer. *1 mark*

d Look at where the tally marks are on the chart.
  i What do you notice about the **amounts** of money people spent at different times in the evening? *1 mark*
  ii Give a reason to explain the difference. *1 mark*

Level 5

The pupils in five classes did a quiz.

The graphs P to T show the scores in each class. Each class had a mean score of 7.
In three of the classes, 80% of the pupils got more than the mean score.

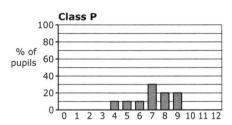

a   In which **three** classes did **80%** of the pupils score **more than 7**?   *2 marks*

b   Look at the graphs which show that 80% of the pupils scored more than 7.

Some of the statements below are **true** when 80% of the pupils scored more than 7.

Write down each statement which is **true**.

All of the pupils scored **at least 2**	
Most of the pupils scored **at least 8**	
Most of the pupils scored **at least 10**	
Some of the pupils scored **less than 6**	

2 marks

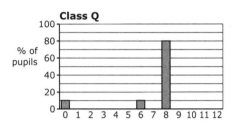

c   In another quiz the **mean score** was **6**.
Copy this graph and complete it to show a mean score of 6.

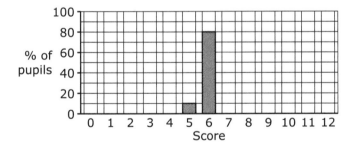

1 mark

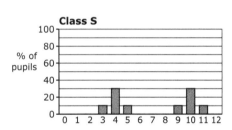

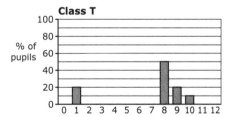

Here is part of a 100 square.

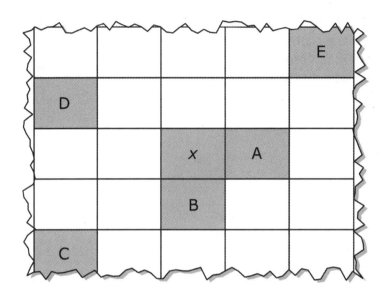

You can describe the position of all the squares using the starting place x.

For example, you can write square A as $x + 1$.

1   Express these squares in terms of x:

   a   B

   b   C

   c   D

   d   E

2 $x - 8$ is two squares to the right of x and one up.

   Describe the position of:

   a $x - 11$

   b $x + 19$

   c $x - 5$

   d $x + 21$

3   If x is 34, what is the value of:

   a   A   **b**   B   **c**   C

   d   D   **e**   E?

A2.2HW Rules of algebra

1 Match each of the eight algebraic expressions with one of the eight sentences.

$2x$ ④   two less than double x ⑦

$x + 2$ ⑥ x multiplied by x ⑤

$\dfrac{x}{2}$ ②   two more than x ⑥

$2 - x$ ③   two less than double x, all multiplied by x ⑧

$x - 2$ ①   double x ④

x^2 ⑤ x less than two ③

$2x - 2$ ⑦   half of x ②

$2x^2 - 2x$ ⑧   two less than x ①

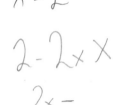

$x^2 - 2$

$2 - x^2$

$x^2 - 2$

$X - 2$

$2 - x$

$2x - 2$

$2 - 2x \times x$

$2x -$

$2x - 2x$

2 Simplify each of these expressions.

You should write each expression using one term.

a $3 \times a \times 4 \times b$ $12ab$

b $5 \times 3a \times 2$

c $2a \times 3b$ $6ab$

d $ab + 3ab$

e $5 \times a \times b - 2 \times a \times b$ $5ab - 2ab$

f $8ab - a \times 4 \times b$

g $3ab - ab \times 2 + a \times 4 \times b + b \times a + 6ba$

h $4 \times 3a \times 5b$

i $a \times 2 \times a \times 5$

j $3a^2b + 2 \times a \times a \times b$

3 By using one of the terms $2y$; $4y$; $5y$; 4, make each of these statements correct:

a $3x \times \underline{4y} = 12xy$ $8y$

b $2 \times 4x \times \underline{2y} = 16xy$

c $5y \times \underline{4y} = 20y^2$

d $3x^2 \times \underline{5y} = 15x^2y$

e $x \times y \times 5 \times \underline{2y} = 10xy^2$

f $3y \times 2x \times \underline{4} = 24xy$

The grids in these questions are taken from a 100 square.

1 What is the value of each shaded square if:

a The two shaded squares total 127.

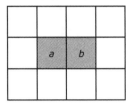

b The two shaded squares total 112.

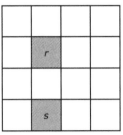

c The two shaded squares total 61.

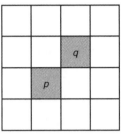

2 Find the total for the two shaded squares.

a

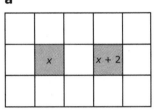

b

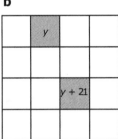

c

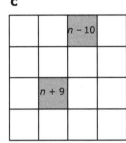

d

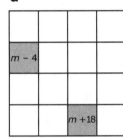

3 The given square is added to the shaded squares. What is the total of the squares?

a

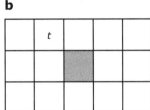

b

c

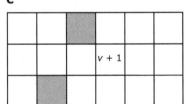

4 Copy this grid.

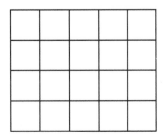

Write expressions in 3 of the squares so that their total is $3n + 8$.

The dice run

This is a board game for one to four players.

Equipment: A dice, counters for each player

Aim: To travel around the board three times

Rules: Each player throws the dice and substitutes the value
into the expression in square 1.
They then move forward the appropriate number of spaces.
If the value is negative then the player moves backwards.
Play continues until one player has gone around the board three times.

START $d - 1$	$2d$	$4 - d$	$2d - 5$	$2d + 3$
$2d - 6$				$10 - 2d$
$4 - d$				$\frac{1}{2}(2d + 2)$
$1 - d$				$8 - d$
$d^2 - 10$	$12 - 4d$	$12 - 2d$	$2(d - 1)$	$3d - 10$

Play the game twice, then answer these questions:

1   Which expression gives you a move of five when you throw a four?
2   Which expressions give you a negative move when you have a small dice throw?
3   Which expressions give you a negative move when you have a large dice throw?
4   Which expressions give you the largest and smallest total when you throw a six?
5   Which expressions give you the largest and smallest total when you throw a two?
6   Which were the best expressions for scoring well?

The Burger Bar sells 3 types of burger:

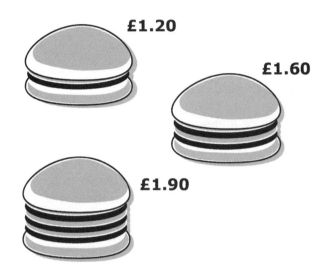

£1.20

£1.60

£1.90

◆ The Super Single (100 g patty)
◆ The Delicious Double (2 × 100 g patties)
◆ The Tremendous Triple (3 × 100 g patties)

In one day they sell *n* singles, *m* doubles and *p* triples.

1 How many burgers did they sell altogether in the day?

2 Each triple has 3 × 100 g patties in it.
How many patties were in the *p* triples sold?

3 How many patties were in the *m* doubles sold?

4 How many patties were sold altogether in the three types of burger?

Single burgers cost £1.20 each.

If they sold *n* singles during the day they would cost *n* × £1.2 or £1.2*n*.

5 How much would *m* double burgers cost at £1.60 each?

6 How much would *p* triple burgers cost at £1.90 each?

7 How much would all the burgers sold during the day cost?

8 **Challenge**

Which is larger: a 100 g patty or a 4 ounce patty?

Explain your answer.

Level 4

The perimeter of this shape is $3t + 2s$.

$$p = 3t + 2s$$

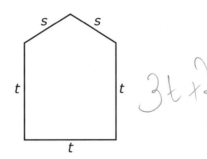

$3t + 2s$

Write an expression for the perimeter of each of these shapes.
Write each expression in its simplest form.

i

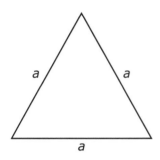

$3a$

ii

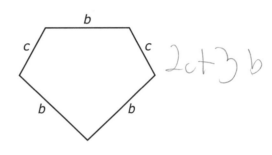

$2c + 3b$

iii

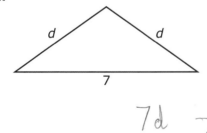

$7d$ $72d$

$7d^2$

iv

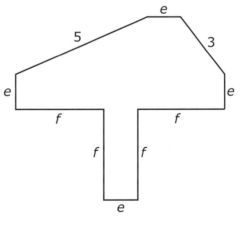

4 marks

Level 5

Write each expression in its simplest form.

a $7 + 2t + 3t$

b $b + 7 + 2b + 10$

c $(3d + 5) + (d - 2)$

d $3m - (^-m)$ *4 marks*

43

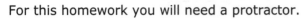

For this homework you will need a protractor.

All the angles should be measured to the nearest degree.

1   Draw these angles and label them.

Write down what type of angle it is (for example acute, or right angle).

a   A$\hat{B}$C = 70°

b   ∠XYZ = 35°

c   ∠P = 120°

d $\hat{Q}$ = 90°

e   M$\hat{N}$O = 216°

f   T$\hat{U}$V = 335°

2   In **a** and **b**, estimate the size of the required angle and then measure it.

a   ∠BAC   **b**   ∠E

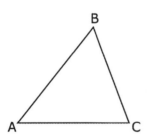

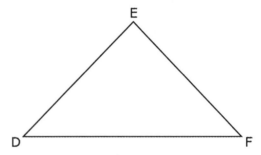

3   **a**   Measure A$\hat{O}$E.

b   Measure E$\hat{O}$D.

c   Measure D$\hat{O}$C.

d   Add together your answers to **a** to **c**.

Write down anything that you notice.

e   Measure A$\hat{O}$B. What could C$\hat{O}$B be?

f   Add together all 5 angles and write down the total.

g   Copy and complete these statements:

Angles on a straight line add to _____°.

Angles at a point add to _____°.

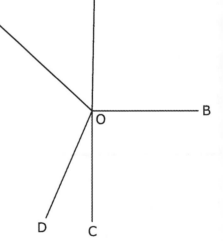

1 Find the given angle in each part, showing your workings clearly.

a B$\hat{E}$C

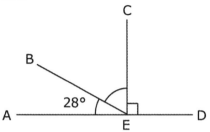

b Q$\hat{T}$R

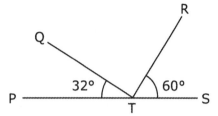

c P$\hat{O}$L

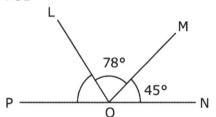

d X$\hat{Z}$Y

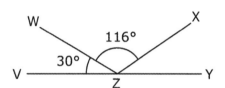

2 Find the angle indicated by a letter, showing your workings clearly.

a $y = 5x$

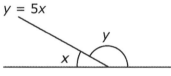

b $z = 4t$

c

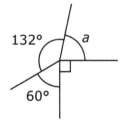

d

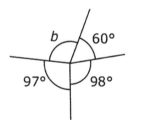

3 Find the given angle, showing your workings clearly.

a $\hat{B}$ **b** $\hat{D}$ **c** $\hat{I}$ **d** J$\hat{L}$K

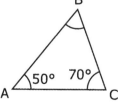

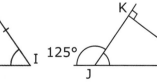

Coordinates and shapes

> **Remember:**
>
> ◆ Area of a rectangle = length × width
>
> ◆ Perimeter of a rectangle = 2 × length + 2 × width

1 The points (⁻3, 1), (2, 1), (2, ⁻2) are three vertices of a rectangle.

Write down the coordinates of the fourth vertex.

Find the area and perimeter of the rectangle.

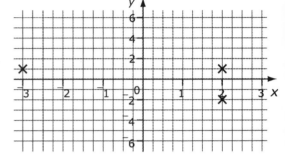

2 Plot these three points: (1, 3) (⁻2, 2), (1, ⁻2).

What fourth point will make:

a a kite **b** a parallelogram

c an arrowhead?

Explain how you chose your fourth coordinate.

Is it possible to make a rectangle? Explain your answer.

3 The points (⁻4, 2), (2, 2), (2, ⁻3) are three vertices of a rectangle.

Write down the coordinates of the fourth vertex.

Find the area and perimeter of the rectangle.

4 The points (⁻4, 3) and (⁻4, ⁻1) are two vertices of a right-angled isosceles triangle.

Write down the coordinates of the third vertex.

Find the area of the triangle.

5 The points (⁻2, 2) and (⁻2, ⁻2) are two vertices of a square.

Write down the coordinates of the other two vertices.

Find the area and perimeter of the square.

6 Draw a pair of axes labelled from ⁻6 to ⁺6.

On your axes draw:

a a square

b a rectangle

c a right-angled triangle

Write down the coordinates of your shapes.

Level 4

a   The time on this clock is **3 o'clock**.
       What is the **size** of the **angle** between the hands?   *1 mark*

b   What is the size of the **angle** between the hands
       at **1 o'clock**?   *1 mark*

c   What is the size of the **angle** between the hands
       at **5 o'clock**?   *1 mark*

d   How long does it take for the **minute** hand to
       move **360°**?   *1 mark*

Level 5

Look at these angles.

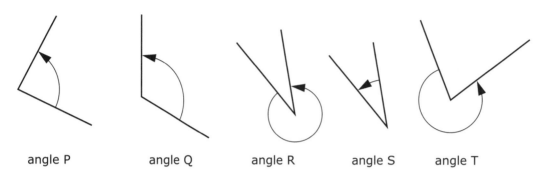

| angle P | angle Q | angle R | angle S | angle T |

a One of the angles measures **120°**. Write down its letter. *1 mark*

b Make a drawing to show an angle of **157°**.
Label the angle 157°. *2 marks*

c 15 pupils measured two angles. Here are their results.

Angle A

Angle measured as	Number of pupils
36°	1
37°	2
38°	10
39°	2

Angle B

Angle measured as	Number of pupils
45°	5
134°	3
135°	4
136°	3

Use the results to decide what each angle is most likely to measure.

i What size is angle **A**? How did you decide? *1 mark*

ii What size is angle **B**? How did you decide? *1 mark*

1 Gina's mum is planning a surprise party for Gina and her friends. She needs to organise some music, but she's not sure what they would like. Explain one way that she could use **primary** data to help her decide, and one way that she could use **secondary** data.

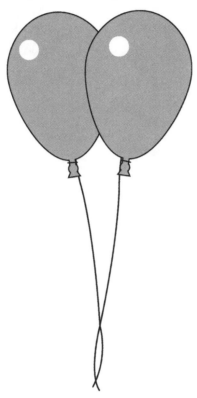

Remember:

Primary data is data you collect yourself.
Secondary data is data you get from another source, like a newspaper or the internet.

2 Which of the two sources of data you have described in question **1** would be best? Write a paragraph to explain why.

3 The kitchen manager at Maypole High School is planning a new set of menus. Describe some of the data that could help her to plan the new menus. Include some examples of primary data, and some of secondary data.

Design a questionnaire to collect some data about an issue that interests you.

Here are some suggestions and hints:

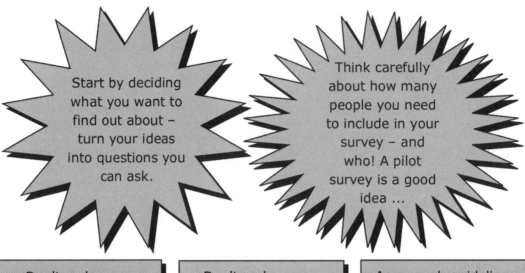

Start by deciding what you want to find out about – turn your ideas into questions you can ask.

Think carefully about how many people you need to include in your survey – and who! A pilot survey is a good idea ...

Don't make your questionnaire too long – or people won't want to complete it!

Don't make your questionnaire too short – it won't give you enough information!

As a rough guideline, 6 or 7 carefully chosen questions should be about right.

What makes a good question?

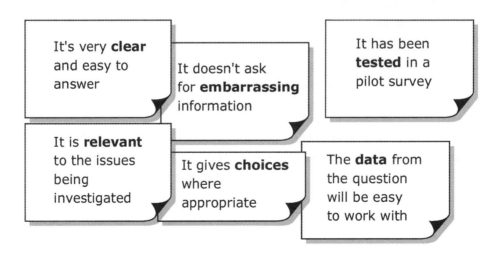

It's very **clear** and easy to answer

It doesn't ask for **embarrassing** information

It has been **tested** in a pilot survey

It is **relevant** to the issues being investigated

It gives **choices** where appropriate

The **data** from the question will be easy to work with

1 Barry is doing a survey about pets. He asks 50 people how many pets they own.

Here are their answers.

0	1	2	2	0	0	3	1	4	3
2	3	1	1	4	5	2	0	0	1
2	4	1	2	1	0	1	3	3	4
1	0	1	2	1	1	0	1	5	0
2	4	1	4	3	0	3	1	1	1

Draw up a frequency table for this data.

2 The heights, in metres, of the 30 players in a rugby game are shown in the table.

1.85	1.74	1.81	1.74	1.92	1.91	1.72	1.91	1.77	1.71
1.88	1.76	1.87	1.82	1.82	1.78	1.89	1.75	1.88	1.87
1.72	1.93	1.81	1.83	1.85	1.89	1.88	1.69	1.79	1.88

Complete a frequency table for this data:

Height (m)	Tally	Frequency
1.65 – 1.69		
1.70 – 1.74		
1.75 – 1.79		
1.80 – 1.84		
1.85 – 1.89		
1.90 – 1.94		

3 A supermarket manager collects data for the amount spent by 16 customers.

£3.55	£28.84	£87.42	£61.20	£1.99	£48.29	£125.67	£42.23
£6.75	£13.44	£71.20	£99.49	£4.49	£10.98	£16.38	£81.39

Draw up a frequency table for the data. Use suitable class intervals.

These heights are measured to the nearest centimetre.

168	178	154	190	183	172	178	157	186	181
179	167	185	176	177	160	169	173	175	179

You can make a frequency diagram for this data.

Firstly, fill in a frequency table, with suitable class intervals.

Height (cm)	Tally	Frequency
150 –	||	2
160 –	||||	4
170 –	┼┼┼ ||||	9
180 –	||||	4
190 –	|	1

> The intervals do **not** overlap.
> The class boundaries are 150, 160, 170...

Secondly, draw up a frequency diagram.

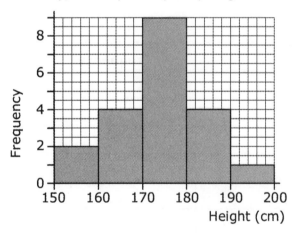

> The class boundaries are used as labels on the Height axis.

1   Draw a frequency diagram for this data which gives the weights of 24 dogs in kg, to the nearest 1 kg.

7	13	9	31	14	25	18	5
19	12	13	11	18	19	17	9
15	11	8	12	15	17	14	22

1 The chart shows the percentage of households in the UK that own video recorders, mobile phones, home computers and dishwashers.

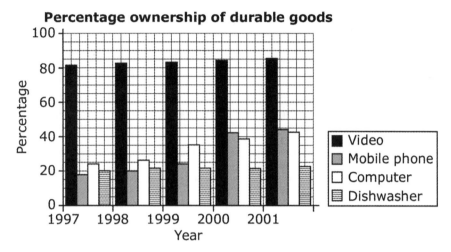

Write a report describing how the ownership of each of these goods changed over the five years shown.

Which item has changed the most? Can you suggest a reason?

2 The chart shows the amount of carbon dioxide produced in the UK in 1970 and 1999.

> It is important to reduce the amount of carbon dioxide gas that is released as it can damage the environment.

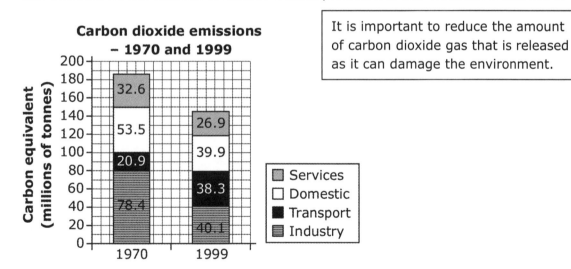

Write a short report summarising the changes shown in the chart.
Try to point out the important features – do not simply list all the figures.

Source: Foreign and Commonwealth Office, UK Datafile 2002

a Lisa works in a shoe shop.

She recorded the size of each pair of trainers that she sold during a week.

This is what she wrote down.

	Sizes of trainers sold						
Monday	7	7	5	6			
Tuesday	6	4	4	8			
Wednesday	5	8	6	7	5		
Thursday	7	4	5				
Friday	7	4	9	5	7	8	
Saturday	6	5	7	6	9	4	7

Use a **tallying method** to make a table showing how many pairs of trainers of each size were sold during the whole week. *3 marks*

b Which size of trainer did Lisa sell the **most** of? *1 mark*

c Lisa said: '*Most of the trainers* sold *were bigger than size 6.*'

How can you tell from **your** table that Lisa is wrong? *1 mark*

Some pupils wanted to find out if people liked a new biscuit.
They decided to do a survey and wrote a questionnaire.

a   One question **was**:

How old are you (in years)?

| 20 or younger | 20 to 30 | 30 to 40 | 40 to 50 | 50 or older |

Mary said: *'The labels for the middle three boxes need changing.'* Explain why Mary was **right**.   *1 mark*

b   A different question was:

How much do you usually spend on biscuits each week?

a lot   a little   nothing   don't know

Mary said: *'Some of these labels need changing too.'*

Draw and label the boxes, writing new labels for any boxes that need changing.

You may change as many labels as you want to.   *2 marks*

c   The pupils decide to give their questionnaire to 50 people.

Jon said: *'Let's ask 50 pupils in our school.'*

i   Give **one disadvantage** of Jon's suggestion.   *1 mark*

ii   Give **one advantage** of Jon's suggestion.   *1 mark*

1   **Multiply by 100**

Find pairs of numbers in the table so that one number is 100 times the other.

2	⁻180	0.2	173	42	420
⁻18	200	20	1730	4.2	0.42
23	230	⁻20	⁻2	17.3	2400
2.3	23 000	0.03	30	⁻200	24
0.7	7	0.3	3	2.4	1700
0.07	3 000 000	30 000	64	17	170

2   Design your own number search for pairs of numbers where one number is 10 times the other.

3   Match up any numbers left over in the grid in question **1**, using the correct operation. You can use numbers which have already been matched up if needed.

For example:

$173 \times 10 = 1730$

Make a set of 12 loop cards which will help you practise the order of operations.

For example:

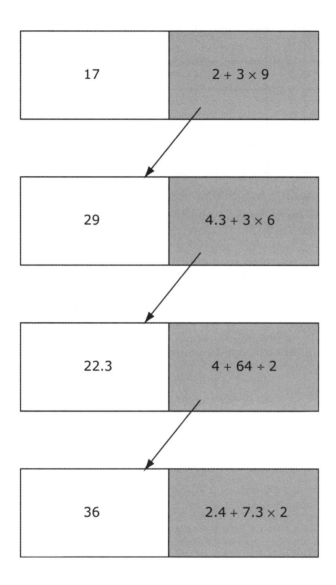

Make sure that the question on your last card has an answer of 17.

The great divide

Box A

256	224
288	264
198	300
240	210
252	216
180	156

Box B

16	12
15	18
9	10
14	13
6	7
8	11

◆ Choose a number from Box A and a number from Box B.

◆ Divide the larger number by the smaller number.

◆ If the answer is a whole number, match the answer in the correct box below and cross off the 2 numbers above. You score the points specified below the box.

◆ If the answer is not a whole number, try again.

◆ The object of the game is to cross off as many numbers as you can, trying to score as many points as possible.

◆ What is the highest number of points you can score?

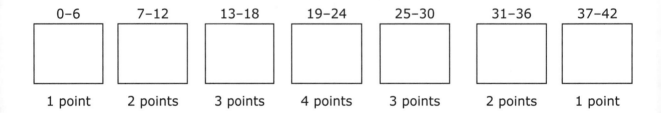

0–6	7–12	13–18	19–24	25–30	31–36	37–42
1 point	2 points	3 points	4 points	3 points	2 points	1 point

N3.4HW Multiplying on paper

You can multiply large numbers using the **grid method** or the standard method:

37×21

$\times$	20	1
30	600	30
7	140	7

So $37 \times 21 = 600 + 30 + 140 + 7$
$= 777$

1 Calculate:

a 23×13

b 34×33

c 52×21

d 73×32

e 83×46

f 76×63

2 Calculate:

a 132×42

b 205×15

c 421×18

d 273×34

Hint: You will need to add an extra column to your grid.

3 Calculate:

a 19.6×35

b 75.7×19

c 363×3.2

d 393×57

e 2671×3

f 697×5.1

Calculate these products:

A   13.4 × 205

E   514 × 1.23

L   9 × 3.27

H   5.4 × 61

N   32.3 × 676

G   5.18 × 97

O   60 × 12.9

P   9.08 × 71

C   3.19 × 927

M   8 × 3.44

R   0.97 × 512

Exchange the answer for the letter next to each multiplication to solve the puzzle.

27.52	644.68	502.46	2747
632.22	632.22	496.64	644.68
29.43	2747	2747	644.68
774	2957.13	644.68	29.43
21 834.8	329.4	632.22	632.22

Dividing on paper

Complete the crossword, using the clues given.

ACROSS

1	$567 \div 7$
3	$736 \div 23$
5	$430 \div 5$
6	$5268 \div 12$
9	$1728 \div 72$
10	$2088 \div 8$
11	$9792 \div 16$
13	$195 \div 15$
15	$923 \div 13$
17	$30\,576 \div 7$
20	$1284 \div 6$
21	$1034 \div 47$

DOWN

2	$14\,768 \div 8$
4	$1452 \div 6$
7	$144 \div 4$
8	$8199 \div 9$
12	$11\,128 \div 52$
14	$1353 \div 41$
15	$936 \div 13$
16	$88 \div 8$
18	$1674 \div 27$
19	$1804 \div 22$

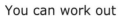
You can work out $193 \div 5$ as

---

a a whole number with a remainder **b** a fraction **c** a decimal

a First approximate:

$193 \div 5 \approx 200 \div 5 = 40$

Then calculate:

$$5\overline{)193}$$
$$\underline{-\ 150} \quad 5 \times 30$$
$$43$$
$$\underline{-\ 40} \quad 5 \times 8$$
$$3$$

$5 \times 38 = 190$

So $193 \div 5 = 38$ remainder 3

b From **a** $193 \div 5 = 38$ rem 3

3 out of 5 is left over.

So $193 \div 5 = \frac{193}{5} = 38\frac{3}{5}$

c
$$5\overline{)193}$$
$$\underline{-\ 150} \quad 5 \times 30$$
$$43$$
$$\underline{-\ 40} \quad 5 \times 8$$
$$3$$
$$\underline{-\ 3} \quad 5 \times 0.6$$
$$0$$

So $193 \div 5 = 38.6$

Make up a division problem of your own to show the meaning of a remainder.
Remember your remainder can be expressed as a decimal, a fraction or a whole number.

This is a scientific calculator:

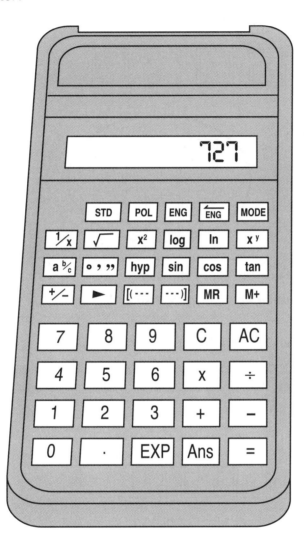

Write a guide to your calculator which could be used by someone who has never seen a calculator before.

◆ Give examples of calculations.

◆ Explain how the ➕ key on the calculator can be used to subtract numbers.

◆ Explain how to use the memory key.

◆ Explain how to use the sign change key.

Here are some number cards:

| 0 | 1 | 2 | 3 | 4 | 5 |

Joan picked these three cards:
She made the number **314**
with her cards.

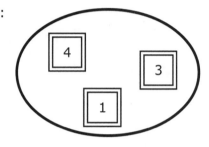

a   Make a **smaller** number with Joan's three cards.   *1 mark*

b   Make the **biggest** number you can with Joan's three cards.   *1 mark*

c   Joan made the number 314 with her three cards.

    i   Which extra card should she pick to make her number **10 times** as big?   *1 mark*

    ii   What number is **10 times** as big as 314?   *1 mark*

d   Andy has these cards:

He made the number 42.5 with four of his cards.

    i   Use some of Andy's cards to show the number **10 times** as big as 42.5.   *1 mark*

    ii   Use some of Andy's cards to show the number **100 times** as big as 42.5.   *1 mark*

———————————————————————— Level 5

a   A shop sells plants.

95p each

Find the cost of 35 plants.

Show your working.

2 marks

b   The shop sells trees.

£17 each

Mr Bailey has **£250**.
He wants to buy as many
trees as possible.
How many trees can Mr Bailey buy?

Show your working.   *2 marks*

1 This is a list of all 25 prime numbers less than 100. Complete the circle of prime numbers.

> **Remember:**
>
> A prime number has only two factors: itself and 1.

(circle of boxes with 2, 71, and 29 filled in)

2 Numbers can be split into a sum of prime numbers.

Can you find two prime numbers that add to make the number 52?

List all the pairs of prime numbers you can find to make 52.

3 **Challenge**

My grandmother said that she could express every square number (up to 144) as the sum of two prime numbers.

Do you agree? Investigate.

1 Match numbers with their squares in the other column.

Two have been done for you.

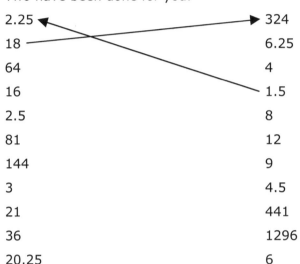

2.25
18
64
16
2.5
81
144
3
21
36
20.25

324
6.25
4
1.5
8
12
9
4.5
441
1296
6

> **Hint:** The direction of the arrow is important. It shows which number is squared.

2 a Complete these columns to find the first 20 square numbers.

$1 \times 1 = 1$ $11 \times 11 = 121$

$2 \times 2 = 4$ $12 \times 12 = 144$

$3 \times 3 =$ $13 \times 13 =$

$4 \times ...$ ...

$5 \times ...$

...

$10 \times 10 =$ $20 \times 20 =$

b Now compare the answers in the same row,

e.g. compare $1 \times 1 = 1$ with $11 \times 11 = 121$

$2 \times 2 = 4$ with $12 \times 12 = 144$

Investigate for all the rows.

What can you say about the unit column values of each answer?

c What would the unit column values be for the squares of 21 to 30?

3 Look at the unit column values in each of these numbers.

i 2102   **ii** 3508   **iii** 2601   **iv** 4257   **v** 3969

a Which could not be square numbers?

b Write down which two numbers could be square.

Are they square numbers?

1   Here are the first, third and fifth patterns in a sequence.

```
    •                   •   •   •              •   •   •   •   •
  •   •               •   •   •   •          •   •   •   •   •   •
                        •   •                  •   •   •   •

   1st                 3rd                        5th
```

a   Draw the 2nd and 4th patterns.

b   Complete the table.

Pattern number	1	2	3	4	5	6	...	10
No. of counters	3				15			

c   Explain in words how the pattern is developing.

d   Predict the number of counters in the 20th pattern and the nth pattern.

2   Here are the rules for 5 sequences. Each of the sequences is also explained in words.
    Match the rule with the explanation and write down the first 5 terms for each sequence.

$2n + 3$ The first term is 5 and each term increases by 2.

$3n + 2$ The first term is 8 and each term increases by 5.

$5n + 3$ The first term is 5 and each term increases by 3.

$3n + 5$ The first term is 7 and each term increases by 2.

$2n + 5$ The first term is 8 and each term increases by 3.

3   Make up a rule for a sequence of your own (e.g. $6n - 2$).

    Explain the pattern in words and write down the first five terms of your sequence.

1 In these questions, use the function machines to work out the outputs and then transfer your results into a table. The first question has been started for you.

a
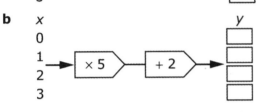

x	0	1	2	3
$y = 3x - 1$			5	

b
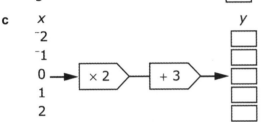

x	0	1	2	3
$y =$				

c
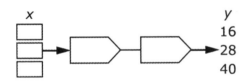

x	⁻2	⁻1	0	1	2
$y =$					

2 Here is a function machine and output:

x		y
		16
		28
		40

a Work out the function machine rule if the input was 1 2 3

b Work out the function machine rule if the input was 2 4 6

c Find at least two more different inputs and rules to get the output 16 28 40

3 Here are three function machines:

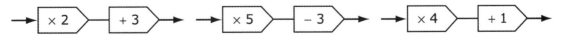

Find the inputs if the output for all three machines is:

a 17 **b** 7 **c** ⁻3

69

1 The crosses marked on the grid represent
the equation of a line.

    a Write down the coordinate pairs and explain
how the *y*-coordinate is related to the
x-coordinate.

    b Write this as an equation.

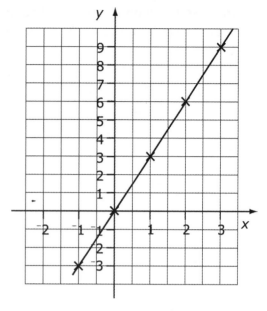

2   **a** Copy and complete this table of results for the equation $y = 2x + 3$.

x	⁻2	⁻1	0	1	2	3
$y = 2x + 3$		1				

    b Write down the coordinate pairs from the table.
Some have been started for you.

       (⁻2,), (⁻1, 1), (0,), (1,), (2,), (3,)

    c Plot these points on a coordinate grid.

      Remember: All of the points lie on the line
$y = 2x + 3$.

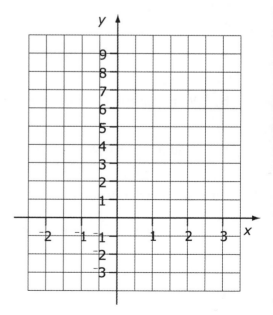

1 Here are 4 different straight-line graphs.

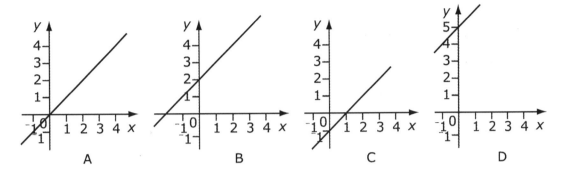

A   B   C   D

a What feature is the same for each line?

b What feature is different for each line?

On one coordinate grid, draw each of the 4 lines (carefully).

c A is the line for the equation of $y = x$.

On the lines carefully mark the equations for B, C and D.

2 Here is a coordinate grid showing the straight-line graph of $y = 3 - x$.

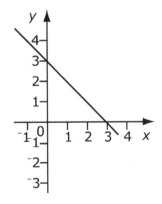

a Carefully copy this onto squared paper.

b Now sketch in the straight lines for the equations

$y = 1 - x$ $y = 5 - x$ $y = {}^-2 - x$

Kath puts **1 small square tile** on a square dotty grid, like this:

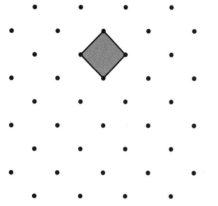

Den makes a **bigger square** with **4** small square tiles like this:

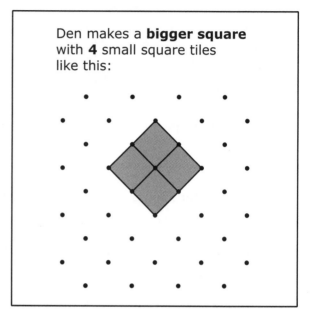

a Scott has **9** small square tiles.

On a square grid, show how Scott can make a **square** in the same way with **9** small square tiles. *1 mark*

b On a square grid, show how to make a **square** with **more than 9** of these small square tiles.

How many tiles are there in your square? *1 mark*

c Huw wants to make some more squares with the tiles.

Write **3 other** numbers of tiles that he can use to make squares.

2 marks

Level 5

a   You pay **£2.40** each time you go swimming.

Copy and complete the table.

Number of swims	0	10	20	30	
Total cost (£)	0	24			*1 mark*

b   Show the information on a copy of the graph below.

Join the points with a straight line.   *2 marks*

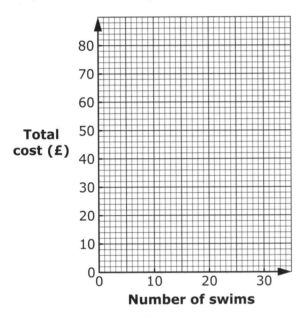

c   A different way of paying is to pay a **yearly** fee of **£22**.

Then you pay **£1.40** each time you go swimming.

Copy and complete the table.

Number of swims	0	10	20	30	
Total cost (£)	22	36			*1 mark*

d   Now show this information on the same graph.

Join these points with a straight line.   *2 marks*

e   For **how many swims** does the graph show that the cost is the
same for both ways of paying?   *1 mark*

Angle problems

Find the value of the letters, giving a reason each time.

1

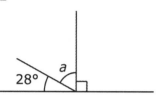

28° a

2

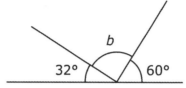

b
32°   60°

3

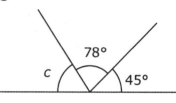

78°
c   45°

4

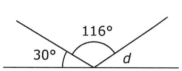

116°
30°   d

5

$y = 5x$

x   y

6

$z = 4t$

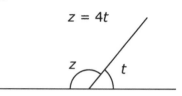

z   t

7

$b = 3c;\ a = 5c$

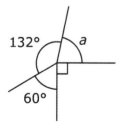

a   b
c

8

$m = 2n;\ l = 9n$

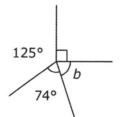

l   m
n

9

$p = 2q;\ q = 3r$

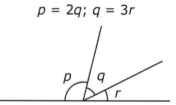

p   q
r

10

132°   a

60°

11

125°
b
74°

12

53°   120°
45°
c

Remember: Angles on a straight line = 180°   Angles in a triangle = 180°

1   Calculate the missing angles. Show all your working.

a

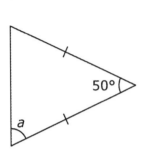

b

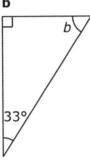

c

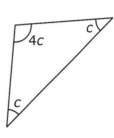

d

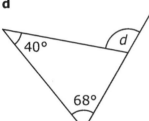

e

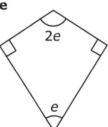

f

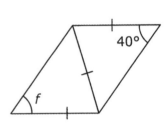

g

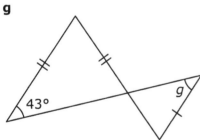

h

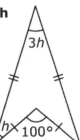

i

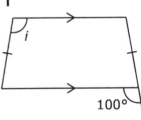

2   **Challenge**

In this triangle, the exterior angle is _____°.

Copy and complete:

Angles on a straight line = 180° so c + _____ = 180°

Angles in a triangle = 180° so $a + b$ + _____ = 180°

Both sets of angles add to 180° so c + _____ = $a + b$ + _____

This simplifies to $c = a + b$

Use this relationship to check your answer to **1d** above.

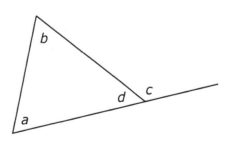

The diagram shows a regular pentagon split into three triangles:

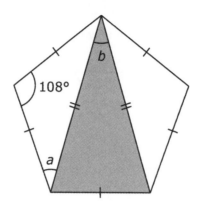

a   Find the value of *a* and *b*.

b   Sheena cuts out the triangles and places two of them together like this:

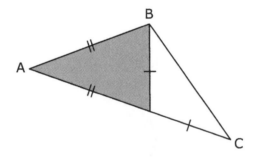

Make a copy of the triangle and mark all the angles on it.

Write down the sizes of angles Â, B̂ and Ĉ.

c   Can you find a different way of fitting the two triangles together to make another triangle?

If you can, sketch your shape and mark all the angles on it.

Are angles Â, B̂ and Ĉ the same size or different?

a What type of triangle is ABC?

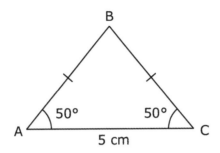

b Write down the size of angle $\hat{B}$.

c Construct the triangle accurately. Use a protractor.

d Check the size of angle $\hat{B}$ by measuring.

e Construct an identical triangle so that one side fits exactly along BC:

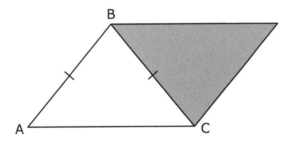

Label the new vertex D.

f Write down the size of each angle: $\hat{A}$, $\hat{B}$, $\hat{C}$ and $\hat{D}$ in your shape.

g What type of quadrilateral is your shape?

h Can you make any other quadrilaterals using two identical isosceles triangles? Investigate.

You can sketch a prism like this:

Draw an end face:

Draw an identical end face above it.

Join the corresponding vertices.

This is the front view: the side view: the view from above:

Its net looks like this:

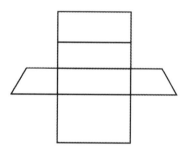

1 **a** Sketch a triangular prism.

   b How many faces, edges and vertices does your shape have?

   c Sketch the net of your triangular prism.

   d Draw its front and side view and its view from above.

2 **a** Sketch a prism with a cross-section of a right-angled triangle.

   b Sketch the net of your prism.

3 **a** Sketch a hexagonal prism.

   b How many faces, edges and vertices does your shape have?

   c Draw its view from above.

4 **a** Sketch a cylinder (circular prism).

   b How many faces, edges and vertices does your shape have?

   c Which two views are exactly the same?

Level 4

Jane wants to design a toy engine.

She makes a rough sketch to show some of the measurements.

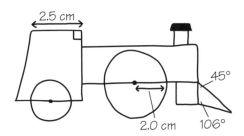

Jane starts to draw the accurate side view.
Here is a copy of her accurate side view.

Copy Jane's side view and finish it.

You will need a ruler, an angle measurer or protractor, and a pair of compasses.

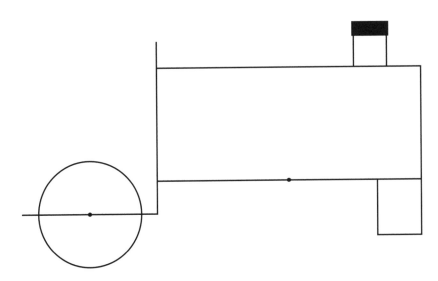

4 marks

Here is a plan of a ferry crossing:

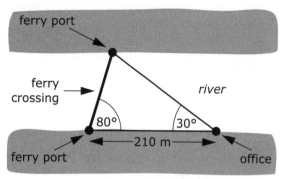

Not drawn accurately

a Copy and complete the accurate scale drawing of the ferry crossing below.

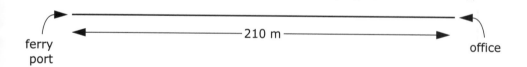

2 marks

b What is the length of the ferry crossing in cm on **your** diagram?

1 mark

c The scale is **1 cm** to **20 m**. Work out the length of the real ferry crossing.

*Show your working and **write the units with your answer**.*

2 marks

1 Copy and complete this table:

Fraction (in its simplest form)		$\frac{5}{16}$		$\frac{17}{11}$		
Decimal (to 3 dp)	0.6				0.95	
Percentage (to 1 dp)			35%			62.5%

2 For each of these pairs of fractions, work out which one is greater.

You will be able to do some of these mentally, others you might be able to do using a written method.

Where the numbers are more difficult you may wish to use a calculator.

Explain the method you have used for each question.

a $\frac{5}{8}$ or $\frac{3}{5}$

b $\frac{21}{16}$ or 1.3

c 1.81 or 1.9

d $\frac{2}{7}$ or 0.3

e $\frac{17}{11}$ or $\frac{27}{17}$

3 I wanted to convert my fraction to a decimal so I divided the numerator by the denominator.

Both numbers in my fraction were less than 40.

The answer came to 0.5862068 on my calculator.

Can you find out the fraction that I started with?

1   Use a mental method to calculate:

   a   70% of £400

   b   30% of 480 m

   c   85% of 780 apples

   d   120% of 22 600 people

   e   240% of 430 kg

2   Alfred owned 240 sheep and 225 cows at the start of the year.

   At the end of the year the number of cows has increased by 24% and the number of sheep has increased by 15%.

   a   What is the total number of cows at the end of the year?

   b   What is the total number of sheep at the end of the year?

   c   What is the total number of animals at the end of the year?

3   Calculate:

   a   12% of 2400

   b   47% of 560

   c   63% of 730

   d   134% of 1240

   e   362% of 130

4   **a**   Calculate $17\frac{1}{2}\%$ of £440. Explain your method.

   b   Design a poster to show how to calculate $17\frac{1}{2}\%$ of £440 using 3 different methods.

1 Calculate these amounts, giving your answer to 2dp where appropriate.
You can work out some of the questions mentally, some using written methods and for
others you may need to use a calculator.

a   35% of £525

b   18% of 450 m

c   73% of 457 kg

d   95% of a right angle

e   125% of £7480

f   109% of 235 litres

g   144% of 3570 m

2 What percentage of:

a   300 pence is 54 pence?

b   25 m is 6 m?

c   3 hours is 45 mins?

d   £220 is 70 pence?

e   12 kg is 4800 grams?

3 **a**   A city covers 850 hectares of land of which 63% is for roads and buildings.
The remaining land is for parks and gardens.

How many hectares is for parks and gardens?

   b   Last year a group sold £12 430 000 worth of CDs.
This year their sales dropped by 38%.

What is the value of their sales this year?

4 For the World Cup of 2002 an estimated 612 million people watched each of the
quarter-final games. For the semi-finals this figure rose by 35%.
For the final it rose by a further 40%.

How many people watched the World Cup Final?

5 Calculate 22% of 1 week. Give your answer in days, hours, minutes and seconds.

1 Work out these amounts using mental or written methods.

    a 7 lemons cost 112 pence. How much would 21 lemons cost?

    b 42 m of tape costs £7.98. How much would 6 m of tape cost?

    c 16 kg of coffee costs £134.40. How much would 40 kg of coffee cost?

    d 84 shirts cost £1007.16. How much would 21 shirts cost?

2 **a** In a game there are 1200 counters, which are either blue or red.

       The proportion of blue counters is 58%.

       How many red counters are there?

    b Morrisey (the cat) donates $\frac{3}{8}$ of his earnings to charity.

       He earns £3400 a year.

       How much money does he donate to charity each year?

    c In a recent survey, 62% of people said that they owned their own car.

       There are 85 000 people in Burnley.

       Approximately how many people own their own car in Burnley?

3 For each of these statements, express the first number as a proportion of the second number.

    a 12 m as a proportion of 30 m

    b £24 as a proportion of £84

    c 30 kg as a proportion of 110 kg

    d 28 mins as a proportion of 1 hour

    e 69 cm as a proportion of 1.84 m

4 **Puzzle**

Soap powder is sold in 3 different sizes:

Small   1.2 kg for £1.15

Medium 4 kg   for £3.68

Large   6.8 kg for £6.32

Which size of packet is the best value for money?

Explain your answer.

1   Cancel down these ratios to their simplest form:

    a   12:33   **b**   14:84   **c**   25:105   **d**   30:165

2   Express each of these as ratios in their simplest form:

    a   A recipe requires 18 oz of tomatoes for every 8 oz
        of peppers – what is the ratio of tomatoes to peppers?

    b   Bernardo has £2300 and Rachel has £475 – what is
        the ratio of Bernardo's money to Rachel's money?

    c   A mother is 31 years old and her son is seven – what will
        be the ratio of their ages in five years' time?

3   Calculate the following:

    a   Rufus and Christabel share 120 tadpoles in the ratio 3:5.
        How many tadpoles will they each receive?

    b   The ratio of women to men in an office is 9:5.
        There are 182 people in the office.
        How many men are there?

    c   Rukia makes a cube out of blue, red and yellow bricks
        in the ratio 3:4:8. She uses between 400 and 410 cubes.
        Calculate the exact number of cubes she has used.
        Explain your answer.

4   Choose a large object in your house.

    Take some measurements of the object.

    Make a scale drawing of the object so that the ratio of the
        lengths in the drawing to the lengths of the object is 1:10.

Level 4

a Find the missing numbers so that the answer is **always 45**.

The first one is done for you.

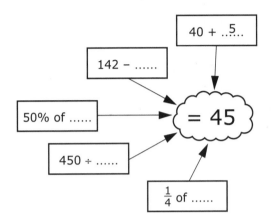

$40 + ..5..$

$142 - ......$

50% of $......$

$450 \div ......$

$\frac{1}{4}$ of $......$

$= 45$

4 marks

b Copy the numbers below and fill in the gaps to make the answer 45.

You may use any of these signs: $+ \ - \ \times \ \div$

$28 \_\_\_ 2 \_\_\_ 31 = 45$

1 mark

Level 5

You can make different colours of paint by mixing red, blue and yellow in different **proportions.**

For example, you can make green by mixing **1 part blue** to **1 part yellow.**

a To make purple, you mix **3 parts red** to **7 parts blue**.

How much of each colour do you need to make **20 litres** of purple paint?
Give your answer in litres.

2 marks

b To make orange, you mix **13 parts yellow** to **7 parts red.**

How much of each colour do you need to make **10 litres** of orange paint?
Give your answer in litres.

2 marks

Number towers

1 Here is a number tower that has been partly filled in. In a number tower you add adjacent numbers together and put the total in the box below.

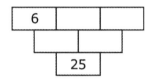

You can fill in different numbers to complete the tower.

a Complete this tower, which has been started for you.

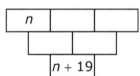

b Draw the original tower three more times.

In each tower, find different numbers to make a total of 25.

2 Use your answer to question **1** to find four ways to complete this number tower.

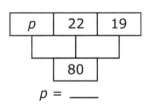

3 Complete these towers to work out the values of the letters.

a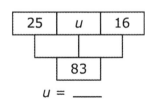

$x =$ _____

b

| p | 22 | 19 |

| 80 |

$p =$ _____

c

| 25 | u | 16 |

| 83 |

$u =$ _____

d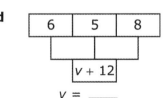

| 6 | 5 | 8 |

| $v + 12$ |

$v =$ _____

Hot crosses

In a Hot Cross the horizontal total is equal to the vertical total.

For example:

	7	
3	6	8
	x	

$3 + 6 + 8 = 17$

$7 + 6 + x = 17$

$x = 17 - 7 - 6$

$x = 4$

1   Place the numbers to complete these Hot Crosses.

a

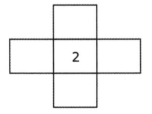

b

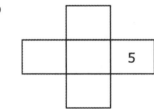

c

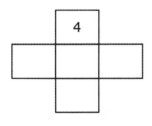

d

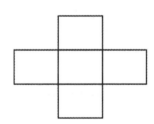

2   These are Hot Cross 20s – each line total is 20.

Write in the missing expression, using x, to make the total 20.

The first one has been done as an example.

	$x + 7$	
$2x$	$3x$	$x + 2$
	$2x - 5$	

$x = 3$

a

	$15 - x$	
$x - 4$		$x + 3$
	$2x - 7$	

$x = 9$

b

$2x$		$x + 5$
	$x - 1$	

$x = 5$

c

$x + 7$		$4 + 2x$
	$3x + 1$	

$x = 2$

Expanding brackets

1 Matching pairs

Draw lines to match the equivalent expressions. One has been done for you.

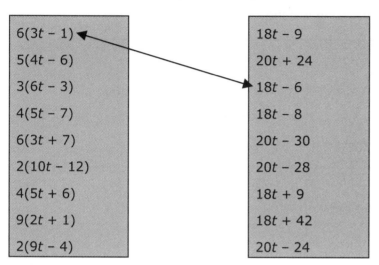

6(3t – 1)	18t – 9
5(4t – 6)	20t + 24
3(6t – 3)	18t – 6
4(5t – 7)	18t – 8
6(3t + 7)	20t – 30
2(10t – 12)	20t – 28
4(5t + 6)	18t + 9
9(2t + 1)	18t + 42
2(9t – 4)	20t – 24

Remember:

4(8x – 3) means 4 × (8x)
and 4 × (⁻3) = 32x – 12.

2 **Tough cookie**

In this question you need to match the number that you multiply the bracket by to give the expression. One has been done for you.

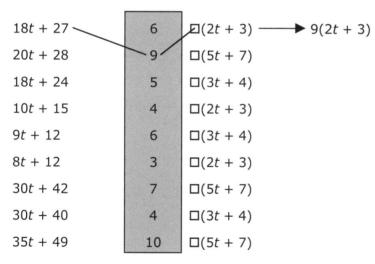

18t + 27	6	☑(2t + 3) → 9(2t + 3)
20t + 28	9	☐(5t + 7)
18t + 24	5	☐(3t + 4)
10t + 15	4	☐(2t + 3)
9t + 12	6	☐(3t + 4)
8t + 12	3	☐(2t + 3)
30t + 42	7	☐(5t + 7)
30t + 40	4	☐(3t + 4)
35t + 49	10	☐(5t + 7)

3 Quickly work out 2999 × 4 … or (3000 – 1) × 4.

Now compare with 4(3t – 1).

What could the t stand for?

Try to quickly work out 796 × 5.

Show your quick method using algebra.

1   Here are 5 problems and 5 equations.

◆   Match each problem with an equation.

◆   Solve each of the equations. One is done for you.

a 2x 110° x 70°	**i** 3x + 180 = 360 2x + x + 110 + 70 = 360 3x + 180 = 360 x = 60°
b x + 40 50 mm Perimeter = 360 mm x x + 60	**ii** 3x + 210 = 360
c I think of a number. I double it, add 120 and then add the number I first thought of. The answer is 360.	**iii** 3x + 120 = 360
d I think of a number, triple it and add 195. The answer is 360.	**iv** 3x + 195 = 360
e (x + 70) cm Area = 360 cm²	3 cm	**v** 3x + 150 = 360

2   Solve each of these equations.

    a   3a + 2 = 23   **b**   4i − 8 = 40   **c**   4e = 10

    d   6n − 20 = 100   **e**   o + 7 = 22   **f**   3q − 12 = 0

    g   3t + 2 = 32   **h**   6u − 8 = 22

Look at your answers to the equations.
List the letters in order of their values, smallest to largest.

What word do you spell?

---

2 boxes balance **1 can**   **2 cans** balance **1 bottle**

   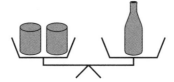

How many **boxes** make each of these balance?

a

b

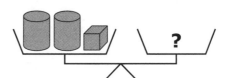

c

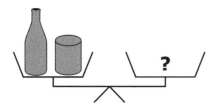

3 marks

d   Joe has these four things:

He wants to put them on the scales to make them balance.

Draw some scales and show where each thing must go.

1 mark

Level 5

Jo is planting a small orchard.

She plants **cherry** trees, **plum** trees, **apple** trees and **pear** trees.

n stands for the number of **cherry** trees Jo plants.

a Jo plants the **same** number of **plum** trees as **cherry** trees.

How many **plum** trees does she plant? *1 mark*

b Jo plants **twice** as many **apple** trees as **cherry** trees.

How many **apple** trees does she plant? *1 mark*

c Jo plants **7 more pear** trees than **cherry** trees.

How many **pear** trees does she plant? *1 mark*

d How many trees does Jo plant **altogether**?

Write your answer as simply as possible. *2 marks*

1 Copy each shape and draw any lines of symmetry.

How many lines of symmetry do each of these shapes have?

a

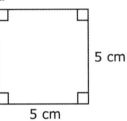

5 cm

5 cm

b

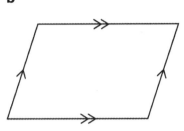

c

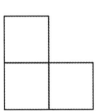

2 Here is a shape made out of four squares:

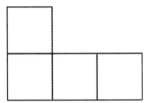

Copy the shape for each part of the question.

Add one square to make a shape with a:

a horizontal line of symmetry

b vertical line of symmetry

c diagonal line of symmetry

3 Copy these diagrams and complete the reflections.

a

M A T H S

Ɐ

b

M
A
T
H
S

T

c

M
A
T
H
S
I

Copy this grid:

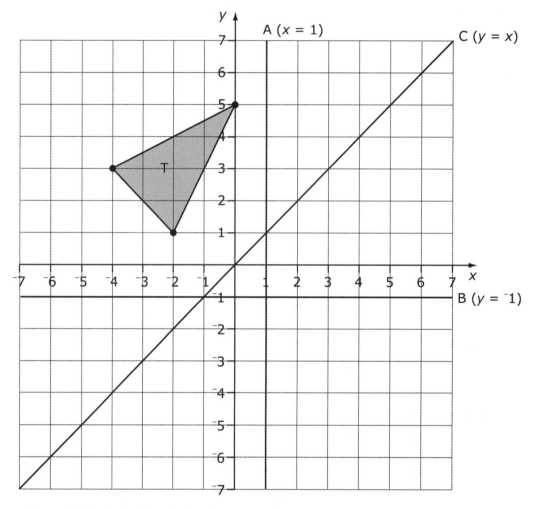

a   Draw the reflection of triangle T in line A. Label it A′.

What are its new coordinates?

b   Draw the reflection of triangle T in line B. Label it B′.

What are its new coordinates?

c   Draw the reflection of triangle T in line C. Label it C′.

What are its new coordinates?

d   **Challenge**

The coordinates of triangle D are (⁻2, 1), (0, 3), (⁻4, 5).

Draw triangle D on your grid.

Draw the mirror line that reflects T onto D.

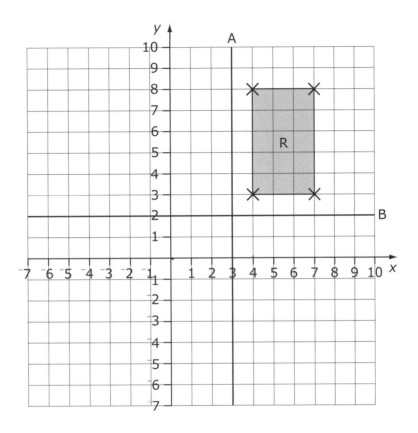

1   Copy the axes drawn on the grid above into your exercise book.
    Draw the rectangle and label it R.

    a   Reflect R in the line A. Label the new shape R′.

    b   Reflect R in the line B. Label the new shape R″.

    c   Translate R five squares to the left and six squares down.
        Label the new shape R‴.

2   Draw axes from ⁻9 to ⁺9. On your axes draw shape A with
    coordinate vertices (2, 2), (2, 7), (5, 7), (5, 4).

    Draw line X, which is vertical and passes through (1, 0).

    Draw line Y, which is horizontal and passes through (0, ⁻1).

    a   Reflect A in the line X. Label the new shape A′.

    b   Reflect A in the line Y. Label the new shape A″.

    c   Translate A four squares to the left and eight squares down.
        Label the new shape A‴.

The grid shows a triangle, T, that has been rotated to shape A.

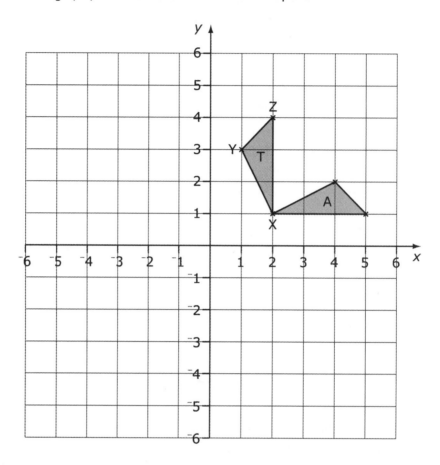

1   a   What are the coordinates of the point corresponding to Y on the new shape?

    b   What is the angle, direction and centre of the rotation?

    c   Describe the rotation that takes A back to T.

2   a   On the same grid, rotate T through 180° about Y. Label your shape C.

    b   What are the coordinates of the point corresponding to Z on your shape?

3   a   On the same grid, rotate T through 90° clockwise about the origin.
         Label your shape D.

    b   What are the coordinates of the point corresponding to X on your shape?

    c   Describe the transformation that moves A onto D.

A square has ...

4 lines of symmetry

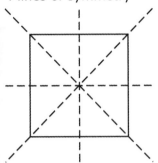

rotational symmetry of order 4

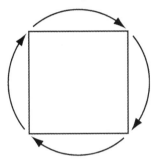

a　Copy this table:

		Lines of symmetry			
Order of rotational symmetry		0	1	2	3
	1				
	2				
	3				

For each of these shapes, write down:

◆　　the number of lines of symmetry

◆　　the order of rotational symmetry

and then write the letter in the correct place in the table.

A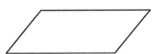

B

C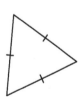

D

E

F

b　Try to sketch a shape that will fit in each blank space in your table.

Copy this triangle onto a coordinate grid:

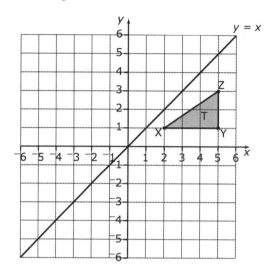

a Write down the coordinates of the points X, Y and Z.

b Reflect the shape in the *x*-axis.

Label your shape B.

Write down the coordinates of its vertices.

What do you notice?

c Reflect T in the *y*-axis.

Label your shape C.

Write down the coordinates of its vertices.

What do you notice?

d Reflect T in the line *y* = *x* shown on the grid.

Label your shape D.

Write down the coordinates of its vertices.

What do you notice?

e Rotate T clockwise through 90° about the origin.

Label your shape E.

What do you notice about the coordinates of its vertices?

Investigate for other rotations about the origin.

f Investigate the relationship between corresponding coordinates following a translation.

Level 4

Catrin shades in a shape made of
five squares on a grid:

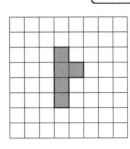

She shades in **1 more square** to
make a shape which has the dashed line
as a **line of symmetry:**

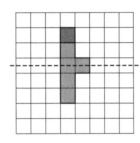

a Copy the diagrams below and shade in **1 more square** to make
shapes which have the dashed line as a **line of symmetry**.

You may use a mirror or tracing paper to help you.

i 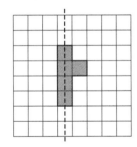   **ii**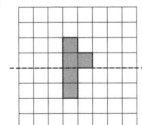

2 marks

b Copy these diagrams and shade in **2 more squares** to make
shapes which have the dashed line as a **line of symmetry**.

You may use a mirror or tracing paper to help you.

i 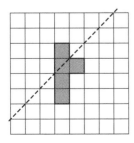   **ii**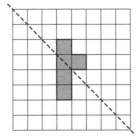

2 marks

An equilateral triangle has
3 lines of symmetry.

It has **rotational symmetry
of order 3.**

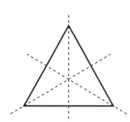

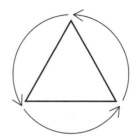

Copy the table below and write the letter of each shape in the correct space.

You may use a mirror or tracing paper to help you.

The letters for the first two shapes have been written for you.

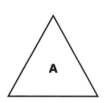

C

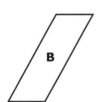

F

Number of lines of symmetry

		0	1	2	3
Order of rotational symmetry	1				
	2	B			
	3				A

4 marks

1   Round each of these numbers to the nearest 100
and to the nearest 10:

    a   346   **b**   821   **c**   1739.4   **d**   12 885

    e   3999   **f**   247 km   **g**   113.62 m   **h**   4196.88 g

2   Round each of these numbers to the nearest whole
number and to one decimal place:

    a   6.37   **b**   2.79   **c**   4.04   **d**   6.638

    e   27.6464   **f**   23.65   **g**   26.81 m   **h**   13.3131 tonnes

3   For each of the following problems, give an answer
to the nearest whole number. Use a calculator if necessary.

    a   290 bottles are to be packed into crates.

        Each crate can hold exactly 12 bottles.

        How many crates will be needed?

    b   Susan has 290 minutes of time left on her mobile.
She wants to enter a special phone competition, to win a new car,
as many times as she can. Each entry to the competition
involves making a phone call lasting exactly 12 minutes.
How many times can she enter the competition?

4   Collect four or five short articles from your local newspaper,
in which exact figures are quoted.
For each article, make up a suitable headline that includes
the figure sensibly rounded.

1   Find all the factors of:

    a   24   **b**   32   **c**   50   **d**   61

    e   71   **f**   120   **g**   144   **h**   220

2   In this arithmagon the numbers in the squares are the products of the numbers on each side.

    Solve this arithmagon.

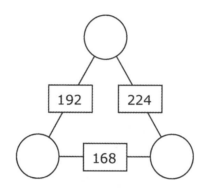

3   Find the highest common factor (HCF) and the lowest common multiple (LCM) of each of these pairs of numbers:

    a   12 and 8   **b**   15 and 20   **c**   28 and 42   **d**   20 and 32

    e   56 and 72   **f**   24 and 84

4   Cancel these fractions to their simplest forms:

    a $\frac{12}{15}$ **b** $\frac{45}{30}$ **c** $\frac{28}{49}$ **d** $\frac{17}{102}$

    e $\frac{135}{153}$ **f** $\frac{126}{322}$ **g** $\frac{331}{289}$

5   **Investigation**

    Find a number with exactly 13 factors.

Remember:

÷ 2   the number ends in 0, 2, 4, 6 or 8
÷ 3   the sum of the digits divides by 3
÷ 4   the last two digits divide by 4
÷ 6   the number divides by 2 and 3
÷ 8   half the number divides by 4
÷ 9   the sum of the digits divides by 9
       3456: 3 + 4 + 5 + 6 = 18 so it divides by 9
÷ 5   the number ends in 0 or 5

---

1   Use the tests for divisibility to find all the factors of:

    a   51   **b**   72   **c**   162   **d**   210

2   Calculate these mentally:

    a 6.7×30 **b** 2.3×4 **c** $168 \div 6$ **d** $252 \div 12$

3   In these arithmagons the numbers in the squares are the products of the numbers on each side.

Solve these arithmagons.

a

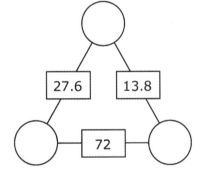

b

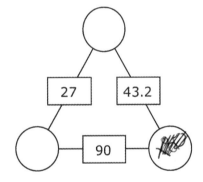

4   **Investigation**

    a   Investigate numbers that divide by 12 exactly with no remainder.

        Find a test for divisibility by 12.

    b   Investigate divisibility tests for 15, 18, etc.

You can multiply decimal numbers using the grid method or the standard method.

For example:

Calculate 3 x 9.25

9.25 = 925 ÷ 100

so 3 x 9.25 = 3 x 925 ÷ 100

Grid method:

Partition 925 into 900 + 20 + 5

	900	20	5
3	3 x 900 = 2700	3 x 20 = 60	3 x 5 = 15

3 x 9265 = 2700 + 60 + 15 = 2775

3 x 9.25 = 2775 ÷ 1000 = 27.75

Standard method:

```
  925
×   3
 2700
   60
+  15
 2775    3 x 925 = 2775 so 3 x 9.25 = 27.75
```

1 The average arm span of an adult with arms outstretched is 1.46 m.
If adults stood in line with arms outstretched, so that their fingertips were touching, how long would the line be if there were:

a 7 adults

b 25 adults

c 200 adults?

2 The distance around the world is approximately 40 000 km.

Investigate how many people you would need to join hands around the world.

1 Calculate:

   a $21.5 \div 5$ **b** $195.2 \div 8$ **c** $86.1 \div 7$ **d** $151.2 \div 9$

   e $163.8 \div 6$ **f** $216.8 \div 8$

2   **a**   Use the digits 1, 4, 7, 9 and 2 to complete this division:

   ●

 ÷

$$\frac{}{6 \quad 1 \;.\; 3}$$

   b   Use the digits 1, 3, 4, 5 and 8 to complete this division:

 ● □ 2

 ÷

$$\frac{}{2 \;.\; \square \; \square}$$

3 **Puzzle**

When I use my calculator to divide one whole number less than 40 by another whole number less than 40, the answer is 1.458333...

What are the two numbers?

1 Make a set of 20 loop cards which will help you to practise finding equivalent fractions.

For example:

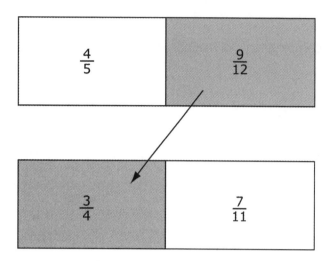

Hint: Make sure that the last card has an answer of $\frac{4}{5}$.

2 Rearrange these fractions in order, starting with the smallest:

$$\frac{2}{3} \qquad \frac{7}{12} \qquad \frac{3}{5} \qquad \frac{5}{8} \qquad \frac{11}{15} \qquad \frac{17}{24}$$

$$\frac{3}{4} \qquad \frac{5}{6} \qquad \frac{7}{10} \qquad \frac{13}{20} \qquad \frac{23}{30}$$

Draw a number line, clearly marking each of these fractions on your line.

Equivalence golf

This is a game for 1 player.

◆ Look at the table below.

◆ At each hole, try to convert the decimal to an equivalent fraction.

The numerator and denominator of your equivalent fraction must both be numbers less than 40.

◆ Write down what you think the answer is in the 'Shot 1' column.

Use your calculator to check if your answer is correct by dividing, for example $\frac{1}{2} = 1 \div 2 = 0.5$

◆ If your answer is correct, move on to the second hole.

If your answer is incorrect, write down your new guess in the 'Shot 2' column. Keep doing this until you have the correct answer for all the holes.

◆ To calculate your score, add up the total number of shots you took for all the holes.

> **Hint:** Par means the average number of shots most people use to get to the hole.

Hole	Target	Par	Shot 1	Shot 2	Shot 3	Shot 4	Shot 5	Shot 6	Shot 7
1	0.2	(3)							
2	0.625	(3)							
3	0.45	(3)							
4	3.4	(3)							
5	0.425	(4)							
6	0.681818...	(5)							
7	0.621621...	(5)							
8	0.46666...	(5)							
9	0.179487	(5)							

My total score = _____ (Par = 36)

All packaged foods have a label giving you nutritional information.
Here are some examples about the fat content of different foods:

> Baked beans: weight **415 g**
> **0.4 g** of fat per **207 g** serving

> Cashew nuts: weight **200 g**
> **48.2 g** of fat per **100 g** of cashew nuts

> Instant hot chocolate: weight **400 g**
> **3.9 g** of fat per **28 g** serving

1 **a**   Which product contains the most fat? Explain your answer.

   b   Put the products in order of fat content, starting with the product
           that contains the least fat.

   c   If Lawrence ate 250 g of baked beans and 55 g of cashew nuts,
           and drank 40 g of instant hot chocolate, how much fat would he
           have consumed?

2 **a**   Look at the labels on food products you eat.
           Work out what percentage of fat is contained in five of your
           favourite foods.

   b   During a normal day, a man is supposed to eat about 95 g of
           fat and a woman 70 g of fat.
           How much of each of your five foods could you eat in a day to
           stay within the recommended daily intake of fat?

Level 4

a A shop sells video tapes for **£2.50** each.

What is the cost of **16** video tapes?

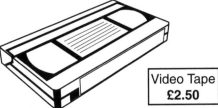

Video Tape
£2.50

1 mark

b The shop sells audio cassettes.

Each cassette costs **£1.49**.

What is the cost of **4** cassettes?

Audio Cassettes
£1.49

1 mark

c **How many cassettes** can you buy with **£12**?   *1 mark*

d The shop also sells cassettes in **packs** of **three**.
A pack costs **£3.99**.

How many packs can you buy with **£12**?   *1 mark*

e Pack of three: **£3.99**   Single cassette: **£1.49**

What is the **greatest number** of cassettes you can buy with **£15**?

You can buy some packs **and** some single cassettes.   *1 mark*

Gwen makes kites to sell.

She sells the kites for **£4.75** each.

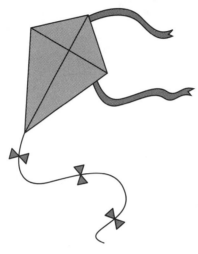

a   Gwen sells **26** kites.

How much does she get for the **26 kites**?

Remember to write down enough working to show you have not used a calculator.

2 marks

b   Gwen has a box of **250** staples.

She uses **16** staples to make each kite.

How many **complete** kites can she make using the **250** staples?

Remember to write down enough working to show you have not used a calculator.

2 marks

Designing a data collection sheet

Simon and Stacey are doing project work.
Simon's project is about the environment.

Here are some of the questions he wants to ask:

◆ Are you worried about the environment?

◆ Do you recycle any of your household waste?

◆ Do you try to save energy at home?

◆ Do you have a garden?

    ◆ If so, do you have a compost heap?

◆ How often do you buy organic vegetables?

◆ How many cars are there in your household?

> Most of these questions just need a Yes/No answer.
>
> One question needs a number to be filled in, and one question gives a series of options to choose from.

Here is part of Simon's data collection sheet.

Name	Worried (Y/N)	Recycle (Y/N)	Save energy (Y/N)	Cars (number)	Garden (Y/N)	Compost (Y/N)	Org. veg (How often – tick)			
							Always	Mostly	Sometimes	Never

Stacey's project is about mobile phones.
Here are some of the questions she wants to ask:

◆ How many people are there in your household?

◆ How many mobile phones are there in your household?

◆ Do you, personally, have a mobile phone?

◆ If you do:

    ◆ What make and model is it?

    ◆ Why did you choose this phone?

    ◆ What network are you on?

    ◆ Is it 'pay-as-you-go' or contract?

    ◆ How often do you use it?

◆ If you don't have one, do you intend to get one?

Design a data collection sheet for Stacey's project.

Drawing bar charts

1   This table shows the amount spent by nine different charities in the year 1998 – 1999.

Charity	Total expenditure (millions of £)
Oxfam	155
National Trust	190
Barnardo's	125
Imperial Cancer Research Fund	102
Cancer Research Campaign	88
Royal National Lifeboat Institution	60
British Heart Foundation	93
Salvation Army	79
Help the Aged	63

Draw a bar chart to illustrate the data.

2   Collect some data about the number of tracks on some CDs.
Record the data in the table below.

CD	Number of tracks

You could collect a different set of data – for example the number of pages in different newspapers and magazines, or the number of lessons you have for each subject you study at school.

Illustrate your data with a bar chart.

Write down two things you notice from your chart.

Remember:

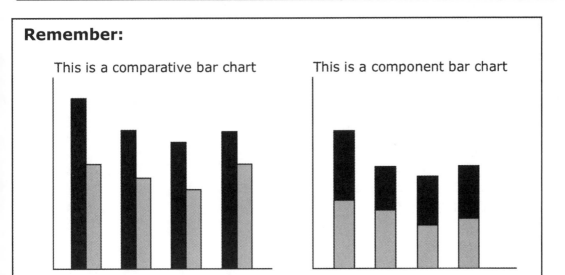

This is a comparative bar chart   This is a component bar chart

1 The table shows the monthly sales figures for two models of car sold by a garage.

Model	Jan	Feb	Mar	Apr	May	Jun	Jul	Aug	Sep	Oct	Nov	Dec
X99	3	4	5	9	12	14	18	10	5	4	3	4
S1	9	8	9	7	8	9	12	9	8	11	10	8

a Draw a comparative bar chart to illustrate the data.

b One of the cars is a five-door hatchback, and the other one is an open-topped sports car.
Write a paragraph saying which is which, and explaining how you know.

2 Two classes collected money for charity over a 7-week period.
The table shows how much each class collected.

Week	Class 7A	Class 7B
1	£3.50	£4.70
2	£4.25	£6.20
3	£9.65	£10.65
4	£10.75	£12.50
5	£12.90	£9.85
6	£8.55	£7.10
7	£6.40	£5.45

Draw a component bar chart to illustrate this data.

Mean, median and mode

1   Fill in the table to show the mean, median and mode for each data set.

Set	Data	Mean	Median	Mode
A	2, 9, 5, 12, 5			
B	1, 3, 9, 26, 5, 4, 3			
C	2, 7, 8, 7, 3, 3, 7, 5			
D	1.2, 3.6, 2.5, 3.7, 9.9, 6.1, 8.8, 2.2			
E	17, 23, 31, 17, 65, 44, 31, 26, 28, 19			
F	152, 147, 147, 149, 141, 152, 160, 158, 159			
G	2.35, 5.45, 6.15, 2.58, 3.95, 4.75, 5.685, 3.175			

2   In set B, which is the value that seems out of place?

Calculate the mean, median and mode without this value.

Do they change?

Which average is now a better representation of the data?

Lower your speed!

A group of parents are campaigning to have 'speed bumps' installed on their road, because they think that most cars on the road are going too fast.

As part of their campaign, they measure the speed of some cars on the road.

Here are their results.

Speed (mph)	Number of cars
20 – 25	3
25 – 30	9
30 – 35	8
35 – 40	6
40 – 45	4
45 – 50	3
50 – 55	1

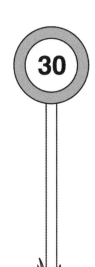

Write an article describing these results, which could go into a newsletter produced by the campaign.

◆ Illustrate the results with a suitable chart. Give a reason for your choice of chart.

◆ Calculate relevant statistics to summarise the data.

◆ Interpret the findings.

◆ Suggest further enquiries the parents may need to make.

Level 4

A pupil recorded how much rain fell on 5 different days.

Results

	Amount in cm
Monday	0.2
Tuesday	0.8
Wednesday	0.5
Thursday	0.25
Friday	0.05

a Copy these sentences and fill in the gaps with the correct day.

  i The **most** rain fell on _____ *1 mark*

  i The **least** rain fell on _____ *1 mark*

b How much **more** rain fell on Wednesday than
  on Thursday? *1 mark*

c **i** How much rain fell altogether on **Monday, Tuesday**
    and **Wednesday**? *1 mark*

  ii Now write your answer in millimetres. *1 mark*

Level 5

a   The graph shows the average heights of young children.

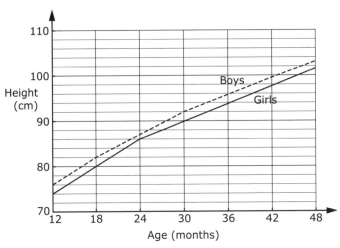

The table shows approximately how much an average **girl** grows each year between the ages of 12 and 48 months.

Copy the table and use the graph to complete it.

Age (months)	Approximate height at start (cm)	Approximate height at end (cm)	Approximate growth (cm)
12 to 24	74	86	12
24 to 36	86		
36 to 48			

2 marks

b   This formula tells you how tall a boy is likely to be when he grows up.

> Add the mother's and father's heights.
> Divide by 2
> Add 7cm to the result.
> The boy is likely to be this height, **plus or minus 10 cm**.

Marc's mother is **168cm** tall.
His father is **194cm** tall.

What is the **greatest** height Marc is likely to be when he grows up? *Show your working.*   *2 marks*

1   A raffle is held at a school fete. 100 tickets (numbered 1 to 100) are sold.
A winning ticket is chosen at random.
Find the probability that the number on the winning ticket is:

   a   6

   b   less than 10

   c   more than 20 and less than 30

   d   greater than 90

   e   even

   f   a multiple of 3

2   Five of the tickets in the raffle are blue, and the other 95 are red.
Keith buys a ticket, and is given a blue ticket with the number 24 on it.
He complains to the person who sold him the ticket:

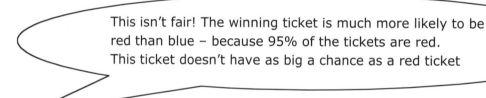

This isn't fair! The winning ticket is much more likely to be red than blue – because 95% of the tickets are red.
This ticket doesn't have as big a chance as a red ticket

Write a paragraph explaining whether you think Keith is right to complain.

3   The 9 letters of the word FRAMEWORK are written on cards and placed in a bag.
One card is chosen at random. What is the probability that the letter chosen is:

   a   F

   b   R

   c   a vowel

   d   a consonant

   e   a letter that comes *after* M in the alphabet

   f   one of the letters of the word WORM?

4   If you choose any word from this sentence, at random, what is the probability that it will have exactly six letters?

Statistical experiments

1 The sketches show the nets of some dice.
The dice were tested by rolling them a number of times and recording the results.
Find the probability of each score for each dice from the results shown.

a

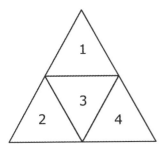

Score	Frequency	Probability
1	13	
2	24	
3	9	
4	4	

b

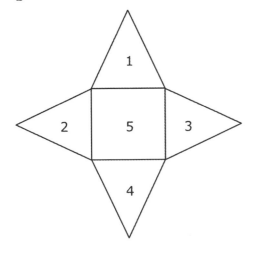

Score	Frequency	Probability
1	17	
2	16	
3	9	
4	18	
5	42	

c

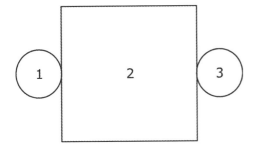

Score	Frequency	Probability
1	4	
2	73	
3	3	

2 Write a short report explaining how to test a dice or spinner.
Say what you need to do to make sure that your results are as reliable as possible.

1   In an experiment, a dice is rolled 60 times and the scores are recorded. The table shows three sets of results:

   ◆   one is a real set of data from a fair dice.

   ◆   one is a set of 'fake' data that somebody made up.

   ◆   one is a set of real data from an unfair dice.

Score:	1	2	3	4	5	6
A	6	25	7	6	7	9
B	9	13	7	12	12	7
C	10	10	10	10	10	10

Say which set is which, explaining your reasons carefully.

2   Each of these experiments or surveys has a problem that will make the results unreliable. Explain what the problem is, and suggest a better way to get the required information.

   a   A scientist wants to find out the average size of fish in a pond.
       She goes out in a boat, and nets the first 5 fish she sees at the surface of the pond.
       She measures each one and returns it to the pond.

   b   A researcher wants to find out how much people use the internet.
       He phones 100 telephone numbers at random.
       If he gets a reply, he asks the person whether they use the internet regularly.

   c   A student wants to know whether people enjoy using big shopping centres.
       She goes to her local shopping mall, and asks 50 people to fill in a questionnaire.

3   Write a short report to explain what you would do if you wanted to check that the results of a weekly lottery were fair.
   Include measures to ensure your report is fair and unbiased.

Level 4

There are 30 cubes in a bag.

Kim takes a cube without looking inside the bag.

She writes down its colour and then **puts the cube back** in the bag.

She does this 30 times.

Kim records her results in a chart:

Red	7
Black	3
White	11
Green	4
Yellow	5

a Kim says: 'There **must** be 7 red cubes in the bag, because there are 7 reds in my chart.'

Explain why Kim is **wrong**. *1 mark*

b What is the **smallest** number of **green** cubes there **could** be in the bag? *1 mark*

c Kim says: 'There **cannot** be any **blue** cubes in the bag, because there are no blues in my chart.'

Explain why Kim is **wrong**. *1 mark*

d Kim takes **one** more cube out of the bag.

What colour is the cube **most likely** to be?

Use the results in the chart to help you to decide. *1 mark*

Level 5

In each box of cereal there is a free gift of a card.
You cannot tell which card will be in a box. Each card is equally likely.

There are **four** different cards: A, B, C or D.

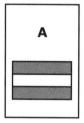
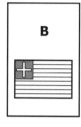
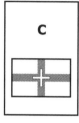
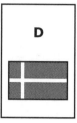

a   **Zoe** needs card **A**.
Her brother **Paul** needs cards **C** and **D**.

They buy one box of cereal.

   i   What is the probability that the card is one that
          Zoe needs?   *1 mark*

   ii What is the probability that the card is one that
          Paul needs?   *1 mark*

b   Then their mother opens the box.
She tells them the card is **not card A**.

   i   Now what is the probability that the card is one that
          Zoe needs?   *1 mark*

   ii What is the probability that the card is one that
          Paul needs?   *1 mark*

Solve the set of equations in each of these questions.

1 **a** $3a + 1 = 10$ **b** $5c = 25$ **c** $6m - 4 = 8$

     d $5r - 5 = 15$ **e** $6s - 1 = 41$ **f** $3u + 15 = 33$

2 **a** $\dfrac{a}{2} = 2\tfrac{1}{2}$ **b** $d + 9 = 20$ **c** $\dfrac{n}{4} = 2$

3 **a** $4h + 7 = 19$ **b** $10 - i = 2$ **c** $3s + 5 = 44$

4 **a** $4a = 10$ **b** $2c + 1 = 22$ **c** $6g = 27$

     d $i + 3.5 = 10$ **e** $8m - 2 = 10$

5 **a** $6a + 17 = 17$ **b** $4h - 10 = 14$ **c** $3m + 10 = 1$

     d $5s - 40 = 15$ **e** $3t - 12 = 0$

6 **a** $6c + 10 = 4$ **b** $3i + 20 = 11$ **c** $8k - 20 = {}^-4$

     d $10 + r = 6$ **e** $2.5s + 2.5 = 15$ **f** $4t + 25 = 1$

7 For each set of equations, list the letters in order of their values, smallest to largest.
Now write the six words as a sentence.

1 The average speed (*v*) is the distance travelled (*s*) divided by the time taken (*t*).

$$V = \frac{s}{t}$$

Find the average speed (*v*) for each of these questions. The first one is done for you.

a A motor cyclist travels 112 miles in 2 hours.

$s = 112$ miles, $t = 2$ hours, $v = \dfrac{s}{t} = \dfrac{112}{2} = 56$ miles per hour

b A swimmer swims 400 metres in 5 minutes.

c A skier travels 2500 metres in 3 minutes 20 seconds.

d An aeroplane travels 5100 kilometres in 6 hours.

e Using the same formula, write your own problem for a bus driver.

(Make sure that the answer is sensible for the speed of a bus.)

2 The volume of a cuboid (box) can be written
volume = length × width × height.
The formula can be written:

$V = l \times w \times h$

Here is a table of results for the volumes of some cuboids.

a Use the formula $V = lwh$ to fill in the gaps.

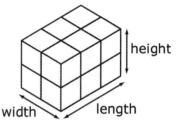

Volume	Length	Width	Height
1 cm³	1 cm	1 cm	1 cm
2 cm³	1 cm	2 cm	1 cm
	1 cm	2 cm	2 cm
	2 cm	2 cm	2 cm
	2 cm	3 cm	2 cm
	2 cm	3 cm	3 cm
	3 cm	3 cm	3 cm
	3 cm	4 cm	4 cm
	4 cm	4 cm	4 cm

b Which of these cuboids are perfect cubes (like dice cubes)?

1 A newsagent charges customers 40p for paper delivery per week, which she pays to the paper-boys and girls.

For each of these questions, work out how much each paper-boy and girl should get paid per week. Give your answers in pounds.

a Tom delivers 42 papers per day.

b Jenny delivers x papers per day.

c Jasbiv delivers 10 more papers than Jenny.

d Last week Jo got paid £22. How many papers did she deliver?

2 These were the results for the school sports day 50 metres sack race.

◆ Solhi finished third in a time of y seconds.

◆ Maggie was 3 seconds faster than Solhi.

◆ Ahmed, who fell over 3 times, was last and took twice as long as Solhi.

◆ Mohammed was 4 seconds faster than Ahmed.

◆ Charlotte, who had a great race, took half the time of Mohammed.

◆ Ebony slipped into fourth place, 5 seconds behind Solhi.

a Find the times for each of the 6 competitors in terms of y.

b List the competitors in order, first to sixth.

A table may help you.

3 For the grand opening last Wednesday the manager ordered 4 boxes of special toys to be included with the kiddies meal.

Each box has n toys.

For each of these questions, work out the number of toys in terms of n.

a How many toys were there at the start of Wednesday?

b On Wednesday they used 88 toys, how many were left?

c On Thursday they used half of the toys available, how many were left?

d On Friday a further 63 toys were used, how many were left?

e On Saturday 8 more boxes were delivered and 180 toys were used. How many were left?

f On Sunday 165 toys were used, how many were left?

g If there were 80 toys in each box, how many were left altogether on Monday morning?

1   Here is a sequence of patterns made up of dots and lines:

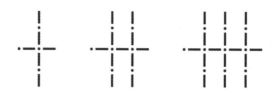

For this sequence of patterns:

a   Draw the next pattern.

b   Complete the tables below.

Pattern no.	1	2	3	4	5	...	n
No. of lines							
Multiples of ?							
Multiples of ? + ?							

Pattern no.	1	2	3	4	5	...	n
No. of dots							
Multiples of ?							
Multiples of ? + ?							

c   Work out the general rule (*n*th term) for this sequence.

2   Here is a rule for another sequence of patterns:

$4n - 2$ counters

Explain in words what is happening with each extra pattern in the sequence.

Draw the first three patterns.

3   ● ● ● ● ● ●   This is the fifth pattern in a sequence.
   ● ●   The first pattern had eight counters.
   ● ●
   ● ● ● ● ● ●

a   Draw the first pattern in this sequence.

b   Work out the general rule (*n*th term) for this sequence.

1   For these double function machines, find the outputs.

a
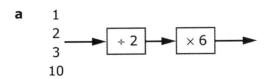

b
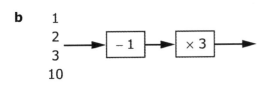

c
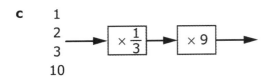

d   Could you simplify any of these combinations into one machine?

If so, what would the one-function machine be?

2   Here is a pair of function machines.

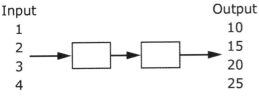

a   Find the missing functions for each machine.

b   Write down the output if the input is *x*.

3   There is a second way to complete the function machines in question **2**.

a   Find a second combination for the function machines.

b   Write down the new output if the input is *x*.

c   For each rule, the output should be the same for the same input, *x*.

Can you show that the answer for **b** is the same in both questions?

Jason is comparing data to see if it is getting warmer in Bristol where he lives.

He looks at the temperature statistics from 1952 and 2002.

Month	J	F	M	A	M	J	J	A	S	O	N	D
Average temperature in 2002	6	7	10	13	16	19	21	21	20	15	11	9
Average temperature in 1952	38	42	48	55	62	66	69	68	66	60	50	46

He is amazed at the difference and then he realises why the data is so different. Can you see why?

In order to compare the temperatures you need to compare either degrees Celsius (°C) with °C or degrees Fahrenheit (°F) with °F.

Jason knows that   0°C is 32°F (freezing point)

10°C is 50°F

50°C is 122°F

and he plots these on a temperature conversion graph, joining them up with a straight line.

He finds that a temperature of 38°F is the same as a temperature of 3°C.

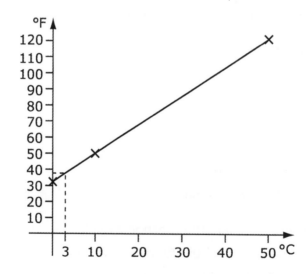

1   On a piece of graph paper, carefully draw a temperature conversion graph like the one above.

2   Now use your graph to convert all of the 1952 temperatures to °Celsius.

3   Compare the 2002 data with that from 1952. What can you say about the differences in temperature?

You will need graph (squared) paper.

a   Copy and complete these tables of values to satisfy the rules:

$y = 2x + 2$

$y = x - 1$

for values of x from ⁻3 to ⁺3.

x	⁻3	⁻2	⁻1	0	1	2	3
$y = 2x + 2$		⁻2					

x	⁻3	⁻2	⁻1	0	1	2	3
$y = x - 1$		⁻3					

b   List the coordinate pairs.

c   Choose a suitable scale and plot these points on a grid (on the graph paper).

d   Draw a line through each set of points.

e   What are the coordinates of the point where the two lines intersect?

f   Draw in the line $x = 3$. What is the shape you have formed?

1 Here is a grid with four different lines:

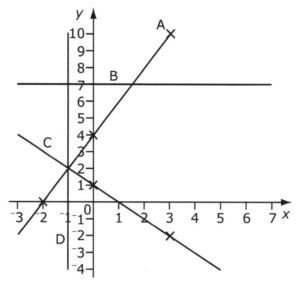

The four lines shown on the grid have equations:

$y = 2x + 4$ $y = 1 - x$ $y = 7$ $x = {}^-1$

a Match each line with one of the equations.

b For each equation, write down one reason why you matched it with a line.

Think about the special features of the equations and of the lines.

2 Six lines have been drawn on this grid.

Look carefully at each line A to F.

Write down the equation for each line.

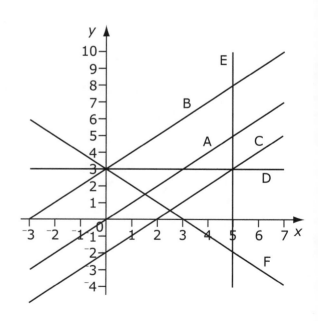

──────────────────────────────── Level 4

Copy each equation and write **one** number at the end of it to make it correct.

Example:

$$26 + 34 = 16 + \underline{\mathbf{44}}$$

a   400 + 150 = 500 + _____

b   14 + 6 = 4 + _____

c   37 − 20 = 27 − _____

d   6 × 5 = 3 × _____

e   38 + 17 = 28 + _____

f   38 − 17 = 28 − _____

g   40 × 10 = 4 × _____

h   7000 ÷ 100 = 700 ÷ _____   *8 marks*

Level 5

Jeff makes a sequence of patterns with black and grey triangular tiles.

The rule for finding the number of tiles in pattern number N in Jeff's sequence is:

number of tiles = 1 + 3N

pattern number 1

pattern number 2

pattern number 3

a   The **1** in this rule represents the **black tile**.

What does the **3N** represent?   *1 mark*

b   Jeff makes **pattern number 12** in his sequence.

How many **black** tiles and how many **grey** tiles does he use?   *1 mark*

c   Jeff uses **61 tiles** altogether to make a pattern in his sequence.

What is the number of the pattern he makes?   *1 mark*

d   Barbara makes a sequence of patterns with **hexagonal** tiles.

Each pattern in Barbara's sequence has **1 black** tile in the middle.

Each new pattern has **6 more grey** tiles than the pattern before.

pattern number 1

pattern number 2

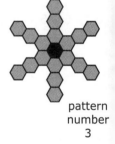

pattern number 3

Write the rule for finding the number of tiles in pattern number N in Barbara's sequence.   *1 mark*

e   Gwenno uses some tiles to make a **different** sequence of patterns.

The rule for finding the number of tiles in pattern number N in Gwenno's sequence is:

number of tiles = 1 + 4N

Draw what you think the first 3 patterns in Gwenno's sequence could be.

2 marks

1   **a**   Construct this triangle accurately:

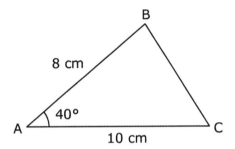

     b   Use your construction to draw this shape accurately:

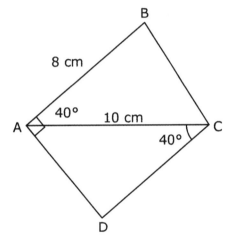

2   **a**   Construct these three triangles:

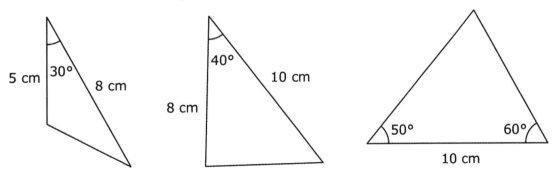

     b   Cut out your triangles and fit them together to make a pentagon.

1 Construct this quadrilateral:

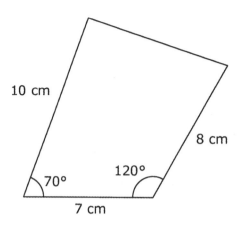

Not to scale

10 cm

8 cm

120°

70°

7 cm

2 **a** Construct quadrilateral PQRS where PQ = 5.5 cm, QR = 4.5 cm, angle P = 90°, angle Q = 80° and angle S = 90°.

b Measure angle R.

c Make a copy of quadrilateral PQRS.

d Cut out your two quadrilaterals.

Fit them together to make a

◆ parallelogram

◆ rectangle

◆ pentagon.

e Are there any other shapes you can make using the two quadrilaterals?

f Sketch each of the shapes you made in **d** and mark on any symmetries.

g Investigate further using the quadrilateral in question **1**.

1 State which of the following nets are:

  a prisms

  b pyramids

  i
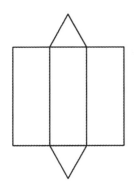

  ii
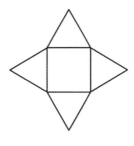

  iii

  iv
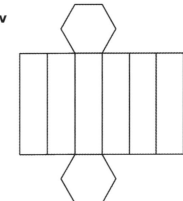

2 Copy and complete each of these diagrams to make the net of the pyramid described.

  a square-based pyramid   **b** tetrahedron

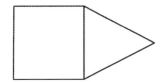   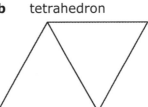

3 Draw other possible nets of the tetrahedron in question **2b**.

Properties of quadrilaterals

Copy the table and list the properties of each of the quadrilaterals.

> Here are some of the keywords you should be using:
> pairs, opposite, adjacent, sides parallel, equal, rotational
> symmetry, reflection symmetry, equal, concave, convex, angles

Quadrilaterals		Properties
Square		
Rectangle		
Rhombus		
Parallelogram		
Kite		
Arrowhead		
Trapezium		
Isosceles trapezium		

Here are three pieces of a shape:

a   Name each piece and describe its symmetry properties.

b   Copy the pieces onto squared paper and cut them out.

Fit the three pieces together, so that they meet edge to edge.

- ◆   Sketch the shape on squared paper.

- ◆   Name the shape.

- ◆   Draw its lines of symmetry.

- ◆   Give the order of rotational symmetry.

c   Fit the pieces together to create different symmetrical shapes.

d   Copy and complete this table for each shape you create.

Sketch	Name	Number of lines of symmetry	Order of rotational symmetry

Tangrams

Copy the diagram and cut out the pieces.

Try to be as accurate as you can.

Cut along the lines.

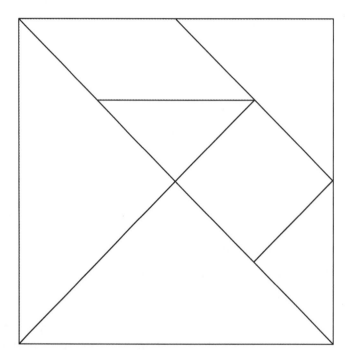

Fit the seven pieces together to make each of these shapes:

◆   rectangle

◆   parallelogram

◆   trapezium with two right angles

◆   isosceles trapezium

◆   triangle

◆   irregular hexagon

◆   irregular pentagon

Draw your answers on squared paper to show how you have fitted
the pieces together.

The diagram shows a box.

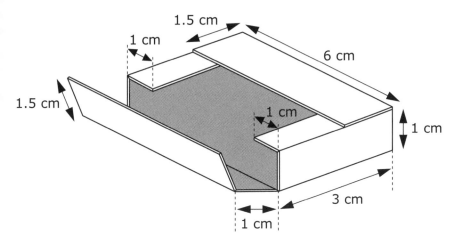

Copy this diagram onto squared paper and complete the **net** for the box.

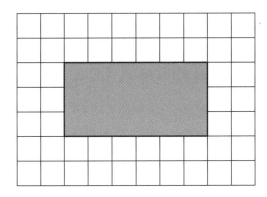

3 marks

Julie wants to make a card with a picture of a boat.

The boat will stand up as the card is opened.

Julie makes a rough sketch of the boat.

It is made out of a triangle and a trapezium.

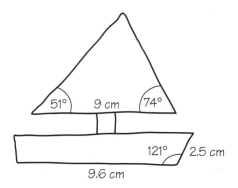

a   On a sheet of paper, make an accurate full size drawing of the **triangle** for the sail.

You need a ruler and an angle measurer or protractor.   *3 marks*

b   Make an accurate full size drawing of the **trapezium** for the boat.

You need a ruler and an angle measurer or protractor.

The bottom of the trapezium, and one edge, have been drawn for you.

Copy this and complete the drawing.

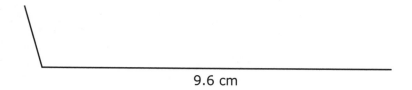

9.6 cm

2 marks